Also by Paulette Maisner:

Feasting and Fasting (with Jenny Pullen)
The Food Trap (with Rosemary Turner)
Excuses Won't Cure You (with Alison Gridland)
Life Is an Elevator (with Rosemary Turner)

The Maisner Centre for Eating Disorders is at:

PO Box 464
Hove
East Sussex BN3 2BN

Tel. (0273) 729818/29334

Paulette Maisner now has consulting rooms in southwest London and there are also many branches of the Maisner Centre throughout the UK. Details of your local branch and information about postal courses and consultations can be obtained by sending a large stamped addressed envelope to the address above.

CONSUMING PASSIONS

Paulette Maisner
with Rosemary Turner

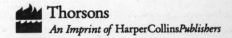
Thorsons
An Imprint of HarperCollins*Publishers*

Thorsons
An Imprint of HarperCollins*Publishers*
77-85 Fulham Palace Road,
Hammersmith, London W6 8JB

Published by Thorsons 1993
10 9 8 7 6 5 4 3 2 1

Paulette Maisner asserts the moral right to
be identified as the author of this work

A catalogue record for this book
is available from the British Library

ISBN 0 7225 2703 9

Typeset by Harper Phototypesetters Limited,
Northampton, England
Printed in Great Britain by
Mackays, Chatham, Kent

To Daniella

Contents

be better equipped to handle the personal side of your life.

Chapter 5 The Maisner Eating Plan
Compulsive eaters need a diet plan designed specially for
them if they are to overcome their problem. This Plan covers
not just what you should eat but why, when and where. Ten
essential steps to getting eating back under control.

PART 3 CAUSE AND EFFECT

Chapter 6 The Triggers, Goodies and Baddies
Certain foods can trigger a binge - how to recognize and
avoid them. Why it is important to include certain vitamins
and minerals and exclude the foods that keep you from
making progress.

Chapter 7 When the Binge Takes Over
Bingeing - a little or a lot - is distressing and harmful. Why
you binge, and how to stop.

Chapter 8 The Bulimic
Bulimia nervosa is not only dangerous for the physical body,
it can become an addictive habit that wrecks lives.

Chapter 9 Seeing the Signs and Offering Support
How to recognize compulsive eating in friends and loved ones,
and the best ways of helping them.

PART 4 GETTING BACK IN CONTROL: COMBATING THE EMOTIONAL EFFECTS OF COMPULSIVE EATING

Chapter 10 Motivation
Good intentions are of little use without motivation. Ways of
moving forward towards success.

Chapter 11 Negative Emotions
Anger, guilt, resentment, jealousy and hate can hold a
compulsive eater back from overcoming her problem. Ways to
turn the negative to the positive.

Chapter 12 Fear
Fear in all its forms - especially fear of food - is the enemy of
the compulsive eater. Taking it a step at a time you can
banish all those fears.

Paulette wishes to thank all her clients (past and present) at the Maisner Centre, who have made this book possible. She also wishes to thank her agent, Frances Kelly, and Matt Fallan for their help during the time of her illness. Finally, her grateful thanks for the help given by the Society of Authors.

The Work of the Maisner Centre

The philosophy and plan for overcoming eating disorders and the examples of case histories used to illustrate them in this book are based on the work of the Maisner Centre for Eating Disorders. (Names and certain personal details of cases have been altered to maintain confidentiality, but the facts are taken from real people suffering very real problems.)

Paulette Maisner is the Centre's principal and it is her personal ability to relate to compulsive eaters and bulimics that makes her method of dealing with the problem so successful.

Paulette became a compulsive eater at a very early age. As a fat, isolated child she had an unhappy childhood. In her early teens she was prescribed amphetamines to combat her weight problem. She soon became addicted and later took to drinking heavily as well. Her brief marriage at an early age was wrecked by her inability to sustain a relationship due to her compulsive behaviour. She went to live in Spain with her young son, working as a translator and continuing her lifestyle of bingeing, purging, drinking and taking pills.

By the age of 40 her life was in ruins. Back in England she suddenly realized she had the choice of continuing in the same old ways or making drastic changes to her life. She chose to make changes and founded the Maisner Centre to help other compulsive eaters, drawing on her unique experience of life in the depths of the obsession pit.

The story of Paulette Maisner's amazing life and the events and experiences that led her to develop her unique philosophy for getting out of the food trap is told in her autobiography, *Life is an Elevator*.

Since founding the Maisner Centre in 1981, thousands of people have turned to Paulette for help, support and advice. Basically these people have fallen into two categories:

1. Those who accept the principles of the Eating Plan and work towards improving their eating habits.

   These people have been prepared to examine what was going wrong in their lives and causing them to binge, and they have been ready to make some far-reaching changes in their attitudes and behaviour.

   These are the people who successfully overcome their eating disorders.

2. The others are those who find endless excuses for not even trying to follow the Eating Plan, for not making changes, for not facing up to their problems.

   These are the people who still have an eating disorder.

Paulette's wide and unique experience of work with compulsive eaters has shown her that there is no middle way, you either succeed or you fail. At first she thought it was not possible to be 'cured' of compulsive eating, that it was only possible to get eating firmly under control. But as the years have gone by she has been amazed and delighted by the number of successful clients who have been able to report that they are truly cured, that compulsive eating is as much a thing of the past as a childhood bout of influenza or measles.

Paulette herself now knows she is cured of her own eating disorders, and she firmly believes that if she - who suffered as severely as anyone possibly could - can really put it behind her then there is no reason why anyone else cannot succeed, particularly if that person seeks out the right attitude, motivation and support.

Paulette's ability to cope with life without bingeing has been tested by many life crises in recent years, in particular when she was diagnosed as suffering from breast cancer and had to undergo an emergency operation and lengthy radiotherapy that totally disrupted her life. This is perhaps one of the most stressful and emotionally challenging things that can happen to any woman, and Paulette discovered she could see it through and overcome it without once suffering the urge to binge to blunt its harsh reality. The additional hurdle of getting through this enormous ordeal without any sort of support from her family made her realize that she truly no longer has an eating problem.

When people come to the Maisner Centre for help they often feel guilty and ashamed of their eating habits. They find it difficult to admit to details of their private thoughts and the negative things that are holding them back and causing them to binge. But when they discover that however low they might have sunk, Paulette has been there and can sympathize with how they are feeling and why they are behaving as they do, it helps to tear down the barriers.

Paulette shares in their delight when they are successful at coming to terms with problems in life; she is not afraid to speak out to those who need to hear some home truths. Workshops bring together people who feel isolated by their eating problems and introduce them to people who share similar problems, often creating an atmosphere of trust and friendship unknown to many caught up in the isolation of a compulsive eating habit.

Both women and men are helped by the Centre, and the Maisner Method has proved equally successful with any degree of compulsive eating, from failed dieters and continuous nibblers to full-blown bingers and those in the grip of bulimia nervosa. Every client is an individual, with individual problems and individual needs. The common element is a general feeling of being out of control where food and eating are concerned.

Introduction

Anyone who has been slimming, dieting and weight-watching for years will know by now that diets do not always work over the long term. You will therefore be relieved to know that this is *not* another diet book: it is a book about getting your eating habits right so that you feel good about yourself and can get on with the important job of enjoying your life.

Food and eating are inextricably tied up with our sense of well-being and emotional security. In these stressful times it is hardly surprising that so many of us express our feeling ill-at-ease with the world through an over-concern with our eating habits and weight. The Eating Plan in this book (Chapter 5) caters sensibly and adequately for your body's needs. It will inspire and support the practical side of your food problem.

Any eating problem, however, is also very much to do with getting your emotional life back under control. Before you can say you no longer have a problem with food you must learn to recognize negative emotions and replace them with positive ones; you must allow yourself to feel good about yourself. Only then will eating and weight no longer dominate your every thought.

People who are lured into erratic eating habits are hungry. Often they suffer from malnutrition and are depleted in many essential vitamins and minerals. Crash diets, severe self-denial and very low calorie intakes leave the body crying out for nourishment. Sooner or later your body will demand to be fed. Hunger is the feeling you get when you are empty, the rumbling in your stomach when you have not eaten for some time: have a meal and the hunger goes away.

But people are often hungry on a deeper level. Emotional hunger is a longing to have the wants and needs of your heart and soul satisfied. Sadly, those with eating problems often cannot distinguish between these two kinds of hunger. They become frustrated when their emotional hunger remains, however much food they swallow.

Learning to recognize one from the other, to discern the needs of the body from the needs of the heart, is an important challenge facing everyone who turns to the comfort of food when life is tough. The following piece, written by a chronic bulimic on her way to recovery, expresses eloquently the distress of emotional hunger which finds its expression in distorted eating patterns.

HUNGER

Hunger is not about food. It is about people.

I had gone hungry for so long I no longer recognized it. I was hungry all the time; physically, emotionally and intellectually. People thought I led a full life because I was out all the time, seeing friends, singing in a choir, doing volunteer work, going to writers' groups and workshops, working out in the gym or aerobics studio until I collapsed in exhaustion.

Activities distracted me and kept my hunger at bay. Yet inevitably there came a time when I had to be alone. I heard the hunger screaming in my head; caught sight of weaknesses which my 'civilized' self could not tolerate: I was shy, insecure, indecisive, dependent, lonely, envious, needy and afraid of rejection.

I had to binge then. I binged to kill my hunger – to deny and suffocate it. Bulimia transformed emotional pain into physical pain, which I could cope with. The hunger disappeared, temporarily abandoned, and I licked my wounds safe in the knowledge that I was too exhausted to feel anything.

Bulimia became the automatic response to non-physical hunger and dissatisfaction. Since my 'civilized' self did not acknowledge the existence of the other, 'weaker' self, there was no conflict. Only the hunger remained, unresolved.

This book offers hope to all hungry people. Read it, learn about yourself, start making the changes your life needs and you will find you have gained control of your life again.

1

Personal Stocktake

1 Self-image

To understand what this book is about, take a look at yourself in the mirror. Do you see reflected there everything your heart desires? Are you filled with joy at the sight of the perfect you, flawless and complete? If so you can close this book now, because you need no further help in learning to love and approve of yourself.

But as even the most beautiful people in the world find something about their appearance that does not satisfy them, it is safe to assume that you are still reading. This means you are not entirely happy with your image. Ask yourself now:

Is this dissatisfaction something you can live with? Or are you limiting your lifestyle and boxing yourself in to ever tighter and tighter corners because of inhibitions about the way you look?

A recent survey reported that 58 per cent of men and women are on some kind of a diet, mostly to lose weight. But another survey states that only one third of these are overweight.

This apparent contradiction can be explained easily. Quite simply, while there are some people who are genuinely obese, whose health would benefit if they lost some weight, there is a vast section of the population who diet just because they are not happy with the way they think they look. They think they have a weight problem because they suffer from low self-esteem. Their problem is *not* weight, it is a poor self-image.

The most beautiful people may despise themselves. Think of those stunning people who could never quite believe in their beauty, like screen goddess Marilyn Monroe. It is not what is going on inside your body that really matters over a lifetime, it is what is happening in your mind. When your soul feels at ease, so does your body.

Getting your self-image right is the key to having the world at your feet, because a poor self-image will restrict and hold you back in every avenue of your life. Physical features cannot hold someone back as much as his or her self-image. Consider Mikhail Gorbachev, who became leader of a huge nation despite a disfiguring red birthmark on his head. Compare his confident attitude to life with that of the man who is afraid to leave his house because he thinks his nose is too big. It is the way we perceive ourselves that makes all the difference.

People who are not happy with themselves want to change. They want to change their lifestyle, their relationships, their ability to cope with everyday life, but they don't know how. The only change they think is within their grasp is to change the shape of their body. So they diet.

In fact, change is easy. The whole universe is in a constant state of change as the planets revolve, the seasons come and go and the weather alters. Our bodies go through a continuous chain of chemical reactions that keep us alive. It is only when we try to resist change that we create huge problems for ourselves. By locking ourselves into rigid thought patterns we forget how to flow with the continuous river of life, free from stress, foreboding and guilt. When food, eating and weight are the mainstay of these unbending thought patterns life becomes a trap, and the only escape is to learn how to resist all negative resistance to change.

HALL OF MIRRORS

Shirley and Kate take a trip to the fair. They enter the hall of mirrors and wander through a maze where differently shaped glasses distort their reflections. They roar with laughter seeing themselves with short bowed legs, long skinny heads, massively expanded hips and long twisted chins. It's a game, they know they are looking at caricatures of themselves and it amuses them greatly.

But why is it that when we play the same game every day with a normal mirror we find it anything but funny? Instead of looking in the glass and seeing a true reflection, every day we see an image of ourselves that is distorted by our emotions, by our desires and by our deep-seated dislike of ourselves. We all do it all the time and it makes us anxious, depressed and frightened. There is always a tendency to exaggerate things we think we don't like about ourselves, seeing only our faults, ignoring our good points. Everyone does it, but some people take it so far it interferes severely with their ability to lead a good life. Are you one of them?

Table 1 HAVE YOU GOT AN IMAGE PROBLEM?

	Always	Sometimes	Never
1. Are you afraid to weigh yourself?	☐	☐	☐
2. Do you feel uncomfortable about using communal changing rooms in clothing shops?	☐	☐	☐
3. Do you believe the shape of your body prevents you from doing things you would like to do, e.g. swimming, cycling, socializing?	☐	☐	☐
4. Do you ask constantly for reassurance that you look good?	☐	☐	☐
5. Do you lie in bed each morning and feel your stomach to see whether it is flatter than it was yesterday?	☐	☐	☐
6. Are most of your clothes too small to fit comfortably?	☐	☐	☐
7. Do you refuse to buy new clothes because you think you are 'too fat'?	☐	☐	☐
8. Do you put off doing things until you are 'the right weight'?	☐	☐	☐

Calculate your score as follows: Always = 4, Sometimes = 2, Never = 0.

SCORING

Less than 7.   You have not got a problem with your self-image. Lucky you—or maybe you have worked hard to develop this positive attitude?

8–15.   Don't allow these few nagging doubts about yourself to grow. Now is the time to nip them in the bud.

16–25.   Sooner or later you will have to face up to the fact that you are not happy with your self-image and are putting all the blame on your real or imagined weight problem. You need to love yourself a bit more.

Over 26.   You have a serious problem and it is probably wrecking your life. Start today investigating all the many ways of learning to like yourself, starting with overcoming hang-ups about your weight. This book will give you lots of help if you are prepared to accept it.

With the changing world, a new image of modern woman has emerged. Gone are the sloping shoulders beloved of romantic novelists, the rounded curves adoringly immortalized on canvas by Rubens and Renoir. Today's woman has so often been portrayed as lean and straight. As she takes on more and more of the roles traditionally held by men it is as if she wishes to leave behind the shape that identifies her as a 'second-class citizen'. Feminine curves have become outdated as women remain the prime victims of fashion.

Nor have men escaped the new obsession to comply to a standard of physical appearance created largely by film producers, model agencies and television commercials. He is expected to be broad-shouldered, lean-hipped, tall and muscular.

These images are rammed home to us constantly until we can easily start to believe that only thin people lead really satisfactory lives. The fat person is still portrayed as a figure of fun, while the slim man drinks beer at the bar and the slender woman eats bars of chocolate. Weight and size have become a national and international obsession – as well as, for many people, a personal one.

People with low self-esteem and a poor self-image may believe they no longer have the right to buy and wear lovely clothes – some avoid clothes shopping totally. They tell themselves that having a broader-than-average bust, pear-shaped thighs or even extra large feet mean the manufacturers and chain stores do not consider them worth catering for. But this is not true these days, as more and more shops are extending their range of sizes.

Yet even the shops that specialize in clothes for larger people are of little use to people whose real problem is self-image. Such people fear even being seen *looking* at larger-sized clothes, although each person's definition of 'larger-sized' is different. A woman who dislikes the image she holds of herself may refuse to look at anything in a size 12 because she wants to be seen buying only size 10 clothes.

Try to learn to really *enjoy* shopping. Choose bright colours and pretty fabrics; and if you can't find something that pleases you, try the simple pleasure of dressmaking. And don't kid yourself: buy or make clothes that *fit*. Comfort is one of the keys to looking good.

What is wrong with a woman being bigger than average as long as she is healthy? Small children love to clamber up an ample lap and cuddle up to a soft chest, and many men will say without doubt they want a lover who is not hard and bony to hold. Yet still the media persist in promoting the myth that the ideal and the successful woman is as thin and shapeless as a stick, goading those who are not naturally of that body shape to wreck their lives in pursuit of the unattainable. It could even begin in the nursery where little girls are given Barbie dolls with long plastic legs, tiny machine-moulded waists and expensive designer wardrobes rather than being left to dress up a soft cuddly teddy bear.

How It Begins

It is easy to see how an obsession with food and eating can develop, and time and again people will say their eating problems began when they went on an inappropriate diet. The desire to be slimmer often begins during the teenage years, or even during childhood, since young minds are particularly impressionable to the dictates of the image-makers. If not kept to realistic proportions, this desire to be a size and shape other than what comes naturally can become a monster that turns and devours the starving dieter. It creates the compulsive eater whose life is overtaken by watching endlessly what she puts or does not put into her mouth.

2 Weight Loss: the Key to Happiness?

How much does food affect your life? Do you only think about lunch when your tummy rumbles and you see it's one o'clock? Or is your morning one long snack (or battle against taking a snack) as you count the minutes until the time you have set yourself as a meal break?

How much of your day is spent thinking about food? Fighting with yourself about what you should and should not be eating? Blaming yourself for your weight, your weak will, your greed? Does your whole well-being depend on whether you have had a 'good' or 'bad' eating day?

Although an estimated seven out of ten women are on some kind of calorie-controlled diet, diets don't work permanently. In fact research has shown that 90 per cent of diets fail to achieve long-lasting results. The weight loss lasts just as long as you can maintain your conscious effort to suppress your appetite and eat less. Sooner or later your control weakens and the pounds roll back on again, often more easily than they did before. Then your guilt makes you feel you must begin another diet and your mind becomes increasingly obsessed with eating and not eating.

Most of the inappropriate slimming diets that lead to eating disorders involve an overemphasis on faddy foodstuffs, excessive calorie counting and drastic denial. They usually impose artificial ways of eating that the body tolerates only until the diet is abandoned, at which point the body once more seeks out its natural weight.

With a lot of hard work and attention to your body it is possible to change your size and shape, and with even more devotion it is possible to maintain this new figure, but too often an artificial eating pattern creates a state of mind that is obsessive. This obsession wrecks relationships, career, family and the whole quality of life.

Table 2 ARE YOU BECOMING OBSESSED WITH DIETING?

1. How many diets have you tried in the last 12 months?
2. How many slimming magazines have you read in the last 12 months?
3. How many diet books have you bought in the last 12 months?
4. By how many pounds has your weight fluctuated in the past 12 months (not including premenstrual days)?
5. How many times have you joined a slimming club?
6. How many times a week do you weigh yourself?

SCORING

Less than 10. Diets and slimming are not an intrusive part of your life.

11–25. You do tend to dwell on thoughts of dieting, but only from time to time; it is not yet a major disruption to your life. Heed the warning signs.

Over 26. Far too much of your time is spent worrying about dieting and thinking about ways to lose weight. It is time you found more fulfilling ways of spending your time and more positive subjects to think about.

56 and over. You are obsessed with dieting and it is severely restricting your ability to enjoy life. Take positive steps at once.

To begin understanding how closely your own eating patterns are associated with the way you live your life, consider the following:

1. Do you believe certain myths about food?
    (a) Brown sugar is better for you than white sugar.
    (b) White wine is not fattening.
    (c) Protein foods are not necessary in a healthy diet.
    (d) You mustn't eat potatoes if you're on a slimming diet.
    (e) Everything bought in a health food shop is good for you.
    (f) Hot meals are better for you than cold meals.
    None of the above is true.
2. Are there certain foods you are afraid to eat?
    (a) Fats and oils:
        Fat equals fat is an exaggeration. Small amounts of fat in the diet are necessary for health; fear of fat is an obsession.

(b) Breakfast:

'If I eat at breakfast I will carry on eating all day.' This cry is heard frequently, but a nutritious breakfast is a very important meal and will ward off the desire to binge later on.

(c) Biscuits:

If 'I can't eat just one' leads to eating the whole packet you should avoid them completely.

There is nothing to fear about food, the problem lies in your attitude towards food, and this can be improved.

3. Do you know the nutritional value (i.e. fibre, protein, unsaturated fat content) of the following?:

(a) A slice of bread

(b) A slice of toast

(c) A chocolate bar

(d) A 4-oz pot of cottage cheese

(e) An apple

(f) One fruit gum

If you have no idea about the nutritional value of any of these foods, perhaps you should learn a little more about general nutrition for the sake of your health.

If you have a rough idea about the nutritional value of each item, you have the basic knowledge needed for sensible eating.

If you can state the exact calorie content of each item, without consulting a book, you probably have an obsession about weight and calories. If this is not already causing you problems you are well on the way to a serious eating disorder.

Constant dieting makes the dieter lose touch with natural feelings of physical hunger, especially if slimming pills or some other artificial substances are used. The desire for food takes over from true hunger and semi-starvation becomes the norm. Those who put themselves through this constant state of self-denial will over-indulge at the slightest opportunity, creating the familiar starve/binge pattern. There is despondency, guilt and you feel worthless as your body slips out of control; then the round of self-denial, dieting and bingeing starts again. The very act of dieting can spark a resentment that makes the body crave more food – as one long-term dieter/binger put it, 'I am at war with myself.'

Some people only feel the desire to binge when they are tired, yet once the habit of bingeing when tired becomes established they can no longer differentiate between feeling tired and feeling hungry. Thought processes become muddled as food and eating, dieting and the desire to binge begin to take over the dieter's mind. Normal life retreats as the food compulsion overwhelms the brain until nothing else matters.

Sally was in her 20s and still living at home when she began to have arguments with her step-father. He said many unkind things to her, including telling her she was fat and she should leave home. Sally went on a crash diet, having convinced herself that the true cause of her unhappiness and her arguments with her step-father was her weight. Yet, precisely because her life was so unhappy, she found it impossible to stick to the diet. Four years later she is still at home, still arguing with her step-father. Her misery and her weight have become welded into one and she has developed a serious eating disorder.

A SHORT PROBLEM

A high proportion of people with a compulsive eating problem tend to be on the short side, usually under 5 ft 2 in. Small women have to watch their weight more carefully than taller ones, so it is easier for them to slip into the trap of an eating obsession. A woman who is 5 ft 8 in can carry an extra stone in weight without it affecting too drastically either her looks or her ability to put on her usual clothes. A petite woman who puts on an extra stone can spread by several inches and be noticeably dumpier. She has to work that much harder at maintaining a figure she can be satisfied with. She is more prone to the risks of an eating obsession.

NATURALLY SLIM

No two people have identical metabolic rates ~ that is, everyone has different desires for food and different ways of digesting and using the food he or she consumes. Some people are naturally slim, it is part of their genetic make-up and is as fixed as being naturally blonde or naturally tall. People who put on weight easily are more likely to slip into a diet trap, yet even slender people can suffer from an eating disorder if their self-image is poor.

OVERWEIGHT

Where the body is excessively overweight, whether this is due to some rare chemical imbalance or overeating, it is important to consider the health risks. Carrying a lot of extra weight, perhaps even twice that considered normal, puts a huge burden on the body's internal organs. It can lead to crippling or fatal illness such as heart or kidney failure; it can also strain or weaken the joints. Being very much overweight is also socially restricting. People tend to stare or make cruel remarks, there can be embarrassing moments like getting stuck in a chair, and even a trip to the shops or going upstairs is exhausting.

In truth comparatively few people reach a state of genuine obesity, compared to the thousands of men and women who consider themselves anything from one to three stone overweight. (See Professor Garrow's weight chart on page 33). They create very real problems for themselves by focusing too much time and attention on the size and shape of their body. These are the people who live to lose weight instead of seeing things the other way round and losing weight to live a better life.

Lauren, who is 5 ft 8 in tall, can maintain a healthy 9 stone 3 pounds in weight without too much trouble. However she is obsessed with the desire to weight 8 stone 12 pounds, and this obsession rules her life. She starves herself, then her control slips and she binges in the classic pattern. Even though a binge in Lauren's world is a teaspoon of jam on a slice of toast, she becomes totally distraught and can find no peace or satisfaction in life all the time the scales show those extra few pounds.

THE PROBLEM IS . . .

If for some reason, perhaps emotional stress or greed, the body is fed more than it naturally wants, it will put on weight. Removing the cause of excessive eating will allow the body to slim down to the size at which it feels most comfortable again.

This sounds fine – just tune in to your body's needs and you will always be your ideal weight. Unfortunately it is rarely this simple.

- For many people the weight their body feels happy at is not in tune with the image they wish to project. If the body is comfortable at 10 stone but social and other pressures create a desired image of nine or even eight stone, a battleground is set up between the will and the body.
- Most people are not truly in touch with their own bodies. The body is the thing you wash and clothe, it carries you around and sometimes it gets tired and ill. We do not really understand its true functions and needs. If it does not act or look the way we want it to we try to change it or impose restrictions on it to fit in with our requirements.
- Life circumstances may conspire to make it impossible to maintain your ideal figure. If you break a leg and have to lie in bed for weeks your figure could change dramatically. If your self-esteem depends entirely on the state of your figure, it could end up as badly damaged as your limb.

Although it is important for your own self-respect to keep your body in good condition, if the point is reached where dieting and exercise are becoming obsessions – the only things that matter in life – then warning bells should begin to ring.

Iris was a successful hairdresser and looking good had always been important to her. She went to exercise classes regularly and watched her diet sensibly so she always looked slim and smart. Then she was diagnosed as having cancer and had to start taking strong drugs which made her put on weight.

Iris was confident enough to realize that even though she was heavier than she'd ever been her health was at stake, her husband still loved her and her many friends had not deserted her, so she turned her attention to fighting her illness and did not worry about her weight.

BEING HAPPY

Could you learn to be happy at the weight you are now? Could you get to know your body and discover the weight at which it feels happiest, and then accept that you can get on with life and be content at that weight?

Answer the following questions:

1. Have you got a goal weight at which you feel you would be happy?
2. When you were last at your goal weight did you feel it was worthwhile?
3. Was your life happier when you were at your goal weight?

If you answered Yes to these questions, then what's stopping you from being that happy person, why did you put the weight back on, and why can't you lose that weight again? Perhaps things weren't really that good, apart from the fact that you were happy with your weight?

If you said No to questions 2 and 3, why are you still hoping to get back to that magic figure that you associate with happiness?

SEEKING A GOAL

Whether you are prepared to accept yourself at a certain weight or not, you are probably at this moment still seeking a goal with regard to your size and weight. Whether that goal is realistic or not can be disregarded for the moment while we look at the far more important issue of the quality of your life while you are on the road towards that goal. Which answer to the following question most suits the way you feel?

Q. Do you enjoy life at present?
A. 1. Yes I am content with my life.
   2. I am content with my life but I want to lose weight.
   3. I am unhappy with my life.
   4. I can't enjoy life because I am overweight.

If you suddenly discovered you only had six months to live, how might that affect the way you answered the above question, and which of the following do you think would be closest to your reaction?

1. I must continue dieting to lose weight.
2. I'm not going to think about my weight any more.
3. To hell with my weight, I'm going to eat and eat and eat.
4. I'm going to make some big changes in my lifestyle.
5. I am going to continue enjoying my life just as I am at present.

Most people who spend a lot of time being obsessed with food and eating (or not eating) tend to go for the second answer when asked to consider this question. Suddenly, faced with a time limit in which to get on with living, weight doesn't matter any more.

It is a fact that none of us knows how long life will last, so why divide the hypothetical from the real? Start *now*, living each day, week and month as if it were your last. Not with reckless abandon, but with a new awareness that it is a waste of valuable living time to be miserable and obsessed.

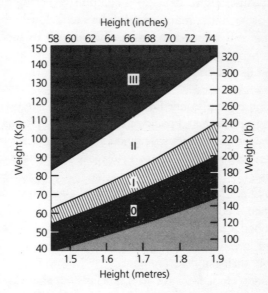

Graph 3.1 *Ideal weights for given heights*

Area 0 is normal weight; areas I, II and III are different degrees of obesity.
Reproduced from *Treat Obesity Seriously* by Professor Garrow, published by Churchill Livingstone.

3 The Symptom, Not the Disease

A weight problem does not necessarily mean you have an eating problem, any more than an eating problem definitely means you have a weight problem.

If you are happy with your life, you like yourself and enjoy satisfying relationships with others, yet the scales say you weigh more than the charts say you should, it is unlikely you have an eating problem. Perhaps you may have a health problem and you should take a serious look at this. But if you are positive about your life you are unlikely to develop a compulsive eating disorder.

On the other hand, many people who are seriously disordered in their eating and trapped in an emotional web of food addiction would not be considered overweight. In fact, they can just as easily be underweight according to the accepted norms.

Linda was grumbling to her friend about how fat she was. Her friend had heard it all before and could not understand what was wrong with Linda. 'Why are you always saying you are fat? – You are really skinny,' her friend said. 'If you were *my* size you really would have something to moan about.'

'But you're not fat,' said Linda, to the total amazement of her friend, who weighed a good four stone more than Linda. In exasperation her friend grabbed a tape measure and put it first round Linda's hips, then around her own. Sure enough the tape showed a good ten-inch difference in their hip measurements.

'But you don't look fat and I do,' Linda insisted. She was so immersed in her compulsive thoughts about food, eating and weight she had lost touch with the reality of what her eyes were seeing.

LIFE DISORDERS

Eating disorders such as bingeing, bulimia and starving are self-imposed reflections of life disorders.

Bingeing is unplanned eating that is out of control. It can be anything from one biscuit to a vast eating session – the amount eaten is irrelevant, it is the fact that eating causes distress that makes it a binge; and it is the degree of distress that determines how serious the problem is.

Compulsive eating is not necessarily a state of continually eating too much, and the term certainly does not apply to the person who loves food, enjoys eating and happily indulges in this pleasure to excess. It does in fact have little to do with the amount you eat. It is the fact that eating concerns you that makes it a disorder. Compulsive eating involves a lot of unhappiness – not just regret when the scales show a few extra pounds, but a whole range of distressing emotions such as guilt, isolation, lack of confidence, fear of failure and a generally poor self-image.

When a food compulsion escalates into *bulimia nervosa* there are further health risks, which are dealt with later in this book. The bulimic makes herself sick after eating, takes excessive amounts of laxatives and/or exercises to excess, all to counteract the effects of eating.

The compulsive eater has much in common with the alcoholic: she often will not acknowledge that anything is wrong, even to herself, and will not seek help until she is at rock bottom. Some people turn to alcohol to drown their troubles, others to drugs, and others sink into depression and suicide or express negative patterns through aggression, violence and crime. Many other people, possibly the majority of those with life problems, focus on food. The compulsive eater becomes helplessly addicted to cramming food into her mouth, even if the consequence is vomiting to relieve the uncomfortable feeling of fullness and to avoid putting on weight.

Negative traits and reasons for abusing food are generally similar to those given for abusing alcohol and drugs: to escape reality, out of boredom, out of habit or due to stress, depression, conflict and crisis, anxiety, anger, emotional pain, insomnia, lack of self-confidence, insecurity or emotional dependency.

The physical effects may also be similar; all three kinds of addiction share such repercussions as: malnutrition, obesity, low blood sugar, problems brought on by overdose, liver and brain damage, self-mutilation, infertility, impaired judgement, lethargy, hopelessness, depression, loss of self-esteem, poor self-image, mood swings, memory loss, loneliness, apathy, breakdown in personal relationships, personal neglect, employment difficulties, isolation, anti-social behaviour, withdrawal symptoms, suicide.

NOT FOR WOMEN ONLY

Much of the information and advice given here is equally relevant to men with eating problems. Men can also suffer from low blood sugar, anger, boredom, unhappy relationships and all the other factors that may build into an eating disorder, although more women seem to be affected, or at least more seek help to overcome their food problems. There are many reasons why women are hit harder than men, apart from the obvious ones such as women being generally more involved with shopping, cooking and providing food for others in their everyday lives. There are also reasons why women are more likely to seek professional help. For example, they are more likely to read magazine articles about the subject and discover the sort of help that is available.

ALL DEGREES

Your attitudes, beliefs and fears about food, weight and eating have probably been with you a long time. The foundations are usually set down in childhood and may have a lot to do with the eating habits of your family and your early emotional experiences.

Although it tends to be the drastic or celebrity cases that hit the headlines, compulsive eating is extremely widespread in all degrees of severity. Maybe your personal eating fight takes the form of the occasional skirmish, maybe it is constant all-out warfare - in either case the battleground is the same: food and weight.

Sometimes it is only in moments of distress that people turn to the larder, or on lonely days to the comfort of a large box of chocolates. When circumstances improve these people feel back in control, their food cravings and desires are no longer a torment. If their underlying life problem has been sorted out they will no longer have an eating disorder. But if the deeper problem has merely been suppressed, the next crisis will cause the eating disorder to emerge and overwhelm them again. In extreme cases the victims of this compulsive eating trap can think of nothing but their relationship with food. For them there is no reality in life, only food, eating, bingeing, dieting, weight. The brain is caught in an endless treadmill of compulsive thought, bringing total misery.

Not everyone with an eating problem goes to this extreme. At one end of the scale there are those whose obsession is so acute it becomes a threat to their life; there are plenty who exist in a dark world completely dominated by their compulsive behaviour and thought patterns. Yet even the person whose problem is not this severe still needs help.

Adele was the sort of person who did not appear to have a weight problem at all. To outsiders she always looked good, and she certainly wasn't fat, but inside she was obsessed with how much she weighed. She had been going to a slimming club regularly for 15 years. At first she had done well, losing over a stone to come within three pounds of her goal weight. But when she reached this point she went on a binge and it took weeks to lose the extra pounds she put on. Time and again the same thing happened; just as that goal came into sight everything fell apart, she would binge and the pounds lost would slip back on again.

Adele did not have a real weight problem. Her main problem was in the way she perceived herself. She was unable to accept herself at anything other than that goal weight – the weight she found impossible to achieve.

'I have no self-confidence at nine stone six, I will only feel good about myself at nine stone three,' she often said. Yet if she felt she'd only be happy and confident at nine stone three why did she binge and sabotage every effort to arrive at this magic number? Was she afraid to find out that weighing nine stone three would not automatically make her content with herself and her life? Or was she so obsessed that she couldn't imagine a life without constant thoughts of eating and weight?

THE FIRST STEP

Before you can do anything about feeling better about your life and controlling your eating, you have to consider whether you have in fact got an eating problem.

Table 3 HAVE YOU GOT AN EATING PROBLEM?

	Often	Occasionally	Never
1. Do you frequently find yourself dieting or trying to lose weight?	☐	☐	☐
2. a. Do you experience panicky desires for certain foods?	☐	☐	☐
b. Are you unable to recognize real physical hunger?	☐	☐	☐
c. Do you eat when you are not hungry?	☐	☐	☐
d. Do you fail to be aware of what you eat?	☐	☐	☐
3. Do you look forward with pleasure and anticipation to the moment when you can eat alone?	☐	☐	☐
4. Do you eat 'sensibly' before others and then overeat when you are alone?	☐	☐	☐
5. Do you have feelings of guilt and remorse when you eat?	☐	☐	☐
6. Do you have feelings of guilt and remorse when you overeat?	☐	☐	☐
7. Do you plan your secret binges ahead of time?	☐	☐	☐
8. If you were eating a cake or sweets, would you eat it all and never leave any (e.g. are you incapable of leaving, say, half a chocolate bar?)	☐	☐	☐
9. Do you enjoy cooking for others although you do not enjoy eating what you have cooked?	☐	☐	☐
10. Do you avoid socializing because of your inability to cope with food?	☐	☐	☐
11. Do you find it difficult to refuse food?	☐	☐	☐
12. When eating with others, do you eat the same as everyone else because you are too embarrassed to ask for what you would actually prefer to eat?	☐	☐	☐
13. Do you feel awkward eating with others?	☐	☐	☐

	Often	Occasionally	Never
14. Are your table manners different when you eat alone than when you eat in public?	☐	☐	☐
15. Are you unable to leave food on your plate?	☐	☐	☐
16. Are your eating habits costing you an excessive amount of money?	☐	☐	☐
17. Do you think about food constantly?	☐	☐	☐
18. Does your well-being depend on whether you have had a 'good' eating day or 'bad' eating day?	☐	☐	☐
19. Are you constantly talking about the diet you are on?	☐	☐	☐
20. Do you count every calorie you eat?	☐	☐	☐

Calculate your score as follows: Often = 4, Occasionally = 2, Never = 0.

SCORING

Less than 10. It really was not worth you buying this book—lucky you!

10–30. There seems to be a problem lurking somewhere, perhaps you should take a closer look and see if you can pinpoint it.

30–60. Yes, you really have got a problem and need help — do write to us and we will send you information about our courses.

Over 60. You'd really better do something about your eating today; it is crucial.

If you think you may have an eating problem you must admit this to yourself and decide to do something about it. The first and perhaps most important thing to understand and come to terms with is that changes will have to be made, and you are the one who will have to make them.

An eating problem is a life problem. Change your life and your eating patterns for the better and your eating disorder will be on the way out - this is the way it works. Unfortunately, most compulsive eaters are locked into the concept that all they need to change is their weight and their lives will improve. It is possible for this to happen, particularly in those cases where the main problem is poor nutrition, where changing to a healthy, nourishing diet works wonders. But the majority of those who have allowed their life problems to be expressed through their eating problems, and their eating problems to exaggerate their life problems, need to do a lot of work. They must change the lifestyle that is colluding with their obsession about food, eating and weight.

Those who fail to improve their lives and their eating are always the ones who refuse to sort out emotional minefields, examine bad relationships or face up to negative habits of thought and action. They say things like:

'I'll do it when I have lost weight.'

'It will be easy when I have my eating under control.'

'I'll do it when I've finished my exams.'

'I'll be able to handle it when the children leave home.'

and so the months and years roll on without any significant improvement in any area.

Julia still lived at home with her mother although she was well into her 30s. She had a dreary job in a factory, no real friends, no hobbies or interests and she was seriously overweight. She longed to meet someone and get married but was convinced this could never happen until she was thin. She spent hours daydreaming about how life could be. But it was only a dream; she was not prepared to try and improve other aspects of her life while she was overweight. During her late teens she had managed to lose a lot of weight, but she did not back this up by becoming more positive in her attitude. When she realized that her knight in shining armour failed to appear when she had reached her ideal weight, and that her life was not happier despite being slim, she slipped back into her old eating habits and just grew steadily older, fatter and less healthy.

Do It Now

Never allow yourself to believe that all your problems will melt away like magic once you are slim. Don't wait until you have a perfect figure to buy that new dress or join an exercise class, and don't fall into the trap of thinking that thin equals happy.

Have you ever really asked yourself just how different your life would be if you weighed a few pounds less? If you are within about a stone of your ideal weight, try answering the following questions. Write down your answers and put them away somewhere. Look at them again in, say, six months' time to see if your attitude has changed at all:

1. Is your ideal weight below that generally given in the medical charts?
   If so, is this because you want to allow yourself room for bingeing and for special occasions like birthdays, Christmas, etc.?
2. What major difference do you think it would make to your life if you were at your ideal weight?
3. Would your children/partner/parents/ love you more if you weighed less?
4. Would you make friends more easily if you weighed less?
5. Would your job be more fulfilling if you weighed less?
6. Would daily chores be less tedious if you weighed less?
7. Would the ideal job/partner/opportunity come along if you were at your ideal weight?
8. Would your financial situation improve if you weighed less?
9. Would you generally find life easier if you weighed less?

You probably said 'No' or 'None' to all or most of the above questions (providing you were honest with yourself), so you will be beginning to realize that weighing a few pounds less would make little difference to the fundamentally important things in your life.

There are always exceptions, of course. If you are an actress, for example, being a certain weight may be crucial to your winning a particular part. But if you sincerely believe that your boyfriend will love you more if you are a few pounds lighter, you are either not seeing the situation clearly or you are in a relationship that is not worth carrying on with. Even if he makes teasing remarks about your figure, he would probably much rather have you happy and the shape you are than tormenting yourself over being slim. If he really only cares about your figure, and doesn't love you for yourself no matter what you look like, perhaps you should be seeking out a more loving and fulfilling relationship.

There is a lot to be learned from the story of Lucinda, who could usually manage to keep her eating under control when she was not in a relationship but whose sensible habits fell apart when she had a boyfriend. Every time she met someone new and he invited her out on a date, her immediate thought was that she must lose weight. She would begin to diet, and that led to bingeing, obsession with food took over her life and the relationship fell apart. She refused to see that the man obviously liked her the way she was when they met, otherwise he would not have asked her out. Tangled emotional processes came into play to wreck each potential relationship, and they expressed themselves through her eating. Lucinda will never break this pattern until she learns to like herself enough to be able to enjoy a relationship. She must learn self-worth, so that she need not feel the need to destroy every relationship by dieting/bingeing.

You must be honest with yourself and see yourself and your life as they are, not as distorted images. You cannot begin to make the changes necessary until you accept that those changes need to be made.

Suzy was furious when it was suggested to her that she had an eating problem. She knew she was overweight, she would be the first to admit she had a weight problem, but an eating disorder – how dare anyone suggest it? She joined a slimming club but left in a temper when she was told she would have to cut out her daily ration of chocolate biscuits. It was something of a ritual at the shop where she worked, at every tea break her group of friends met in the canteen for a gossip and a plate of biscuits. She was not going to forgo this habit and be the odd one out just because she had a weight problem. The canteen chats were the highlight of her day, her children had grown up and married and her husband was morose and aggressive, so she had nothing to look forward to at the end of the day except the television and her evening meal.

Suzy made no progress in losing weight, in fact the more she worried about dieting the more weight she seemed to gain. Even when she was diagnosed diabetic she still angrily refused to make any changes in her life. It took a long time for her to realize and accept that she did in fact have life problems that she was expressing through her eating habits. Gradually, with help and support, she broke through the wall of her own anger and introduced positive elements into her life. She was able to separate the pleasure of good company from the pleasure of eating biscuits, and learned that one could exist without the other. But, more radically, she gave up her tiring job in the shop and concentrated on developing her neglected talent for writing. She also became more assertive in her relationship with her husband and expanded her social life. To her surprise she finally discovered that not only was she now much happier with her life and liked herself more, but she had also lost three stone in weight.

Suzy's story is typical of so many people. They become so entrenched in a rut of their own negativity that they can see no way out until they discover that shifting the focus of their attention from food and eating to other areas of living unlocks the door and they become free to develop into whatever they want to be.

2

Action Plan: Combating the Physical Effects of Compulsive Eating

4 Your Body Chemistry

Going on a 'normal' diet won't help the compulsive eater or bulimic. Only an eating plan designed specifically for people with eating disorders will prove successful in the long term. After many years of working with compulsive eaters it has been proved time and again that the method that works is based on:

1. eating the right kinds of foods and
2. eating frequent and regular meals.

It is around these basic rules that the Maisner Eating Plan (described in the next chapter) has been devised. Thousands of people have discovered that by committing themselves to following the Plan they can get their eating under control while continuing to transform other aspects of their lives for the better.

Anyone who suffers from an allergy or a particular illness may have to adopt a set of rules about what he can and cannot eat so as not to aggravate the condition. Members of certain religions also have rules laid down about which foods they are not allowed to eat. The same is true of those with an eating disorder: there are guidelines that must be understood and followed. Compulsive eating does not go away on its own. It is a serious problem that will only get worse if it is not taken in hand and controlled.

The human body is an extremely complex machine run by an intricate network of chemical reactions, most of which are in some way inter-dependent. When everything is harmoniously balanced the body functions well and is healthy – but throw one area off-line chemically and the knock-on effect is felt physically and emotionally.

It is of course vital to work on your emotional and life problems during the journey back to controlled eating, but your best efforts can be seriously undermined if your body chemistry is out of balance. For this reason it is essential to make a serious commitment to the Eating Plan. It will sort out your physical imbalances, leaving you better equipped to handle the personal side of your life.

Get it right and it will work for you. Within an amazingly short time you will begin to emerge from the binge/starve trap, and that is when other aspects of your life will start to seem more manageable as well.

Before getting started on the actual Eating Plan, it is a good idea to understand a little bit more about how your body actually works. The basic dogma of 'Eat and get fat; starve and get thin' may be true in principle, but in fact this is far too simplistic an approach - nor does it work, as most dieters and all compulsive eaters know to their cost.

Some slim people are very active and use up great amounts of calories in their daily lives. Others have poor appetites and do not eat sufficient food to allow them to put on weight. Still others lead lazy, greedy lives and still stay slim. This could be to do with their body chemistry: they may have a larger number of the more effective *mitochondria* (tiny powerhouses present inside the body's cells). These extra mitochondria tend to concentrate in the brown adipose tissue or 'brown fat'. (Brown fat is the kind that burns off calories to keep the body warm rather than the better-known white fat used for storage - it is this white fat that is the enemy of dieters.) Where there is plenty of brown fat tissue in the body, overeating only stimulates the cells to generate extra heat and burn off the surplus, thus keeping the body slim. Where there is less brown fat extra food is stored in white fat cells, creating the fat we all recognize.

It may be true to say that nobody came out of a concentration camp fat, but this terrible thinness lasted only as long as the victim's imposed starvation. Research has shown that those who survived and went back into a world where food was freely available tended to put on weight more easily than those who had never known starvation. And that was not just because they ate more to make up for what they had missed, their body had actually adapted to store fat more easily.

This is exactly what happens when someone goes on a crash diet. The body does not know the difference between social injustice and social fashion - in other words, not knowing about the mode to be slim, whenever food is denied it the body assumes there is a famine and adapts for survival. It does this by becoming more economical with the little food it does receive. This means lowering the body's metabolic rate (the rate at which it burns up calories) and storing up any available fat.

Whether a binge is prompted because the body is starving or only thinks it is starving makes little difference to the binger - all she knows is that she does not feel in control of her body's urge to be fed.

THE GLYCOGEN TRICK

One of the signs of a compulsive eater is that her body weight is erratic; it can vary surprisingly quickly during a phase of bingeing or starving. This has in fact little to do with fat and everything to do with another substance, called *glycogen*.

Despite the claims of wonder diets that promise you will lose 'ten pounds in a week', a crash regime hardly touches those fat cells that are the body's stronghold against famine. When food is in short supply, glycogen is the fuel used to supply the body with immediate energy. Glycogen is stored in solution with water in the body's muscles and in the liver. On average the body carries about eight to ten pounds of glycogen solution. This is what is lost over the first days of strenuous dieting when the pounds seem to come off comparatively quickly. You may have noticed when you begin a strict diet that you seem to want to pass a lot of water: this is the excess fluid being discarded when you use up the glycogen it was carrying.

However, at this point your body starts receiving signals that it is hungry, and this is when the urge to binge becomes overpowering. Bingers who have been starving nearly always feel an overwhelming desire for carbohydrate foods that give a quick energy boost, such as sugar, chocolate, bread, cereals, biscuits and cakes. When this happens your body is trying to replace blood sugar.

If, however, the initial urge to binge is overcome and the strenuous diet continues, it is still not fat that tends to be lost. The next to go is lean tissue such as muscle, particularly if the person is not taking much exercise and the muscles do not appear (to the body) to be needed. Because the body is programmed for survival, when food is denied it, it slows down. There are feelings of fatigue and the metabolic rate drops so less food is needed. If the dieter then begins eating again at this point, the body is likely to store any excess in the form of fat rather than replace the lost lean tissue, so the person ends up fatter and less fit than before starting the diet.

The best way to maintain blood sugar at a moderate but *steady* level is to have a diet high in protein. *Spare* protein is broken down to urea (voided in the urine) plus fat plus carbohydrate. This process is slow but steady and avoids the swings and roundabouts of a diet high in sugar (see the next chapter for more details).

Figure 1 illustrates the difference between losing weight at a sensible rate and swinging between crash dieting and bingeing. After a healthy diet there is still a good proportion of muscle and bone while, although an unhealthy dieter may weigh the same as the healthy dieter, the quality of her body tissue is greatly inferior.

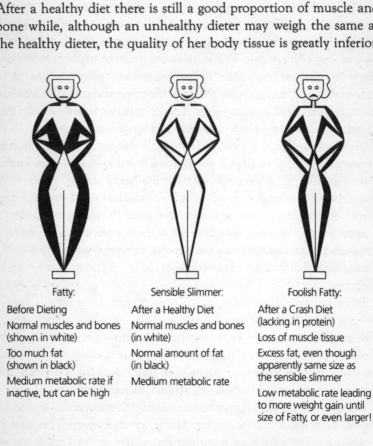

Fatty:	Sensible Slimmer:	Foolish Fatty:
Before Dieting	After a Healthy Diet	After a Crash Diet (lacking in protein)
Normal muscles and bones (shown in white)	Normal muscles and bones (in white)	Loss of muscle tissue
Too much fat (shown in black)	Normal amount of fat (in black)	Excess fat, even though apparently same size as the sensible slimmer
Medium metabolic rate if inactive, but can be high	Medium metabolic rate	Low metabolic rate leading to more weight gain until size of Fatty, or even larger!

Figure 1 *Losing weight sensibly vs losing weight too quickly*

Jeanette's story is one that many people will recognize. She had never been slim but for many years got on with her life quite happily, not bothering too much about her figure. In her late 20s Jeanette and a friend decided to go along to a slimming club they saw advertised in the newspaper. They thought it would do them good to lose a bit of weight.

To begin with Jeanette lost ten pounds, and so she stopped going to the club but continued calorie-counting on her own. Gradually she realized she was thinking more and more about what she was and was not eating, she was weighing herself twice a day and her moods began to depend on what the scales told her. Each time it looked as if she had put on a pound she panicked and went on a binge. Within a year she weighed a stone more than before she had joined the slimming club!

Jeanette's next attempt to lose weight took the form of a visit to a diet doctor who prescribed slimming pills and put her on an 800-calorie-a-day diet. Jeanette lost ten pounds. Then came Christmas: she awarded herself a diet-free fortnight and put on two stone. A lot of this was in fact extra fluid in response to the low-calorie regime she had been following, but again she panicked and returned for more slimming pills. This time they didn't seem to be working for her and Jeanette realized she had developed a severe compulsive eating problem.

The erratic swings between starving and bingeing had confused her body. Until then it had been getting clear messages about the amount of food it would receive each day and the amount of energy it was supposed to provide and it organized itself to keep Jeanette's weight fairly stable. But when the dieting started it could no longer be guaranteed regular nourishment. Her body learned to expect famine at any time, and adjusted its expectations accordingly, storing fat more easily against the lean times.

Being a slave to the scales is the cause of many unnecessary binges. Although actual body weight can fluctuate quite a lot, especially during times of under- or overeating, this is mainly to do with fluid levels rather than actual fat. It is almost impossible to lose more than two pounds of fat in a week. Two pounds of fat equals 7,000 calories a week, or 1,000 calories a day. If the average woman needs 1,800 calories a day to function efficiently, a diet of 800 calories a day would mean a shortfall of 1,000 a day. This represents the limit to which the average body can lose fat, so if the scales show a sudden drop of half a stone overnight it is definitely *not* all fat that has been lost. Drastic overeating can put on weight at more than two pounds a week, but if the scales show a huge weight gain it is likely that much of this will be fluid.

The following example illustrates this:

A doctor prescribes his patient appetite-suppressant pills and advises her that only 800 kcal per day should be consumed.

Bearing in mind the average metabolic rate of a woman is 1800 kcal a day, this represents a loss of 1000 kcal per day (which equals two pounds of fat per week).

Full of good intentions, the patient buys a book on calorie counting to help her keep a strict eye on her caloric intake.

The patient consumes no more than 800 kcal per day. *However*, the doctor failed to recommend that much of this should be made up of *protein* foods. Intake of protein is vital because it prevents the loss of protein tissue when dieting.

The patient chooses foods that are low in protein, preferring small amounts of her favourite high-calorie refined carbohydrate foods instead.

She is *apparently* very successful, losing six pounds in Week One of the diet, four pounds in Week Two, three in Week Three and two more in Week Four, for a total of 15 pounds.

But looking at this more closely we can see that much of this weight loss has been false:

- Week One: weight loss = 6 lb
  False loss = 4 lb: 3.5 lb water from glycogen + .5 lb muscle tissue (protein + water)
- Week Two: weight loss = 4 lb
  False loss = 2 lb: 1.5 lb water from glycogen + .5 lb muscle tissue
- Week Three: weight loss = 3 lb
  False loss = 1 lb: .5 lb water from glycogen + .5 lb muscle tissue
- Week Four: weight loss = 2 lb
  Mainly fat, a little muscle
- Total False Loss: 7 lb

By the end of the four weeks this woman has also lost a great deal of protein tissue. If instead she had eaten 60 g a day of pure protein she would not have lost *any* protein tissue and she would have lost a genuine two pound per week. As shown, she has actually lost almost no fat. She will also regain the false seven pounds rapidly, a seriously disheartening result.

For foods that are safe and sensible to eat, see page 66.

When we understand that our bodies are subtle, reasoning, adapting entities, not simple push-button machines, we can start to treat them with more respect and learn to work with them instead of fighting against them. The body will always win, it has been programmed to survive and is infinitely resilient to every attack we make on it. Learn to use your body chemistry correctly and you will achieve the weight that your body is happy at. At this weight you will no longer physically have the need to binge. Learning to live at that weight even if it does not seem to comply to standards set by social conventions (that is, even if you still think you are too fat) is a separate but equally important issue. You need to get to grips with this issue before you can truthfully say you no longer have an eating problem. If you have convinced yourself that you want to weigh six-and-a-half stone (and it is unlikely that your body will be happy at that weight unless you are of extremely small build), your life will be a constant battle between your mind and your body. You have to come to terms with the fact that to overcome the urge to binge you must accept a realistic body weight.

ENERGY NEEDS

How much energy a body needs to work to maximum efficiency can be influenced by all sorts of factors. Taking extra exercise will increase your calorific requirements, not just because of the extra energy needed to perform the physical functions but because an increased demand for oxygen will boost your metabolic rate on a long-term basis, burning up fat faster.

Mental and emotional states also affect how much food you are likely to need, because feeling low or getting depressed will decrease your body's needs, even though perversely this is when many people eat more. Depressed people tend to use up less calories because they are generally less active, they may walk more slowly, take less exercise and perhaps go to bed earlier.

Sometimes depression may come on as a result of depressing the body's physical functions through dieting. Most people have had the experience of sitting around all day feeling gloomy, then going out for a brisk walk in the fresh air and feeling better. This, in miniature, is what happens if your body is starved and its natural functions depressed: exercise, oxygen and food will give it a lift.

A fit person with good muscle structure and little fat will have a much higher metabolic rate than someone who, although he may weigh the same, has less muscle and more fat. This is because the fit person's body functions more efficiently.

THE IMPORTANCE OF EXERCISE

To avoid carrying around unwanted fat cells, not only must you persuade your body that it does not need to stock up for impending famine but you also need to raise your metabolic rate so that calories are burned off more quickly. This means increasing your oxygen supply. The best way to do this is vigorous exercise.

Animals bred for meat are discouraged, usually forcibly, from taking exercise so that their meat will have a good layer of fat running through it. Wild animals and those allowed plenty of freedom and exercise have much tougher meat, with muscle and sinew in place of fatty deposits. (This difference is what distinguishes beef from venison.) To be like a racehorse ready to win rather than a sow waiting to go to the bacon factory you have to get physically fit and take as much air and exercise as possible – without overdoing it or becoming addicted to exercise, of course.

Modern life makes it very easy to be physically lazy. Driving instead of walking, putting clothes in a machine instead of scrubbing them by hand, pushing a vacuum cleaner instead of sweeping and beating the carpets – nevertheless there is no need to go back to hours of boring chores to get fit: while the washing machine is cleaning your clothes, you can go swimming or to an aerobic exercise class.

Aerobic exercise (at least three times a week) will strengthen your heart and lungs, promote the growth of blood vessels and generally lift your body's energy balance to a higher level.

Replacing fat cells with muscle will not necessarily make you weigh less – but if you are following the rules of the Eating Plan you will no longer be weighing yourself continually and panicking about what the scales say. However, you'll be toned up so you'll look and *feel* better. You will notice a difference in your measurements and in the way your clothes fit. Exercise can also redistribute weight, as flab in unwanted places is replaced by muscle tissue lying close to the framework of the body, so you are likely to be more pleased with your shape. You will feel and be more alive, happier and more self-confident.

The fitter you get and the more in tune with your body, the more likely you are to turn away from the wrong foods and begin to prefer foods that are good for you. You will be more likely to eat only when you experience real hunger, and after a good exercise workout you are not so likely to be tempted to nibble. When you have used your body hard you will find that you can more easily relax and will sleep more soundly. Over a period of time regular aerobic exercise can increase your body's metabolic rate. The human body is designed to be exercised and functions more efficiently if it is pushed hard regularly rather than over-cossetted.

Working in an office all day, tackling a pile of ironing or doing the weekly shopping are all physically tiring but they do not burn up fat cells. This kind of exercise, which does not make you out of breath, is fuelled by blood sugar and, when this is used up, more is obtained by breaking down glycogen – which is easily replaced at the next meal.

The sort of aerobic exercise that calls for physical endurance – such as a long brisk walk or swimming as far as you can without stopping – will be fuelled quite differently, from the body's fat stores. This fat is not automatically replaced once the exercise ceases. Regular exercise of this kind will ensure that lean tissue in the form of muscle replaces those unnecessary fat cells.

If you have not exercised recently, if you are overweight, over 40 and/or have any medical condition (especially a history of heart disease) do consult your doctor before taking up any form of vigorous exercise. It is also not recommended that you exercise after you have been bingeing.

Almost every sports centre and lots of private clubs run aerobics classes, although some of these seem to attract glamorous women in designer leotards who might make a beginner feel awkward. If the class you go to makes you feel fat and foolish that is the fault of the instructor, so find somewhere more friendly where the emphasis is on fun and fitness.

It is a good idea to go to a proper, experienced instructor whose classes are not too large. You could damage your joints and/or muscles if you exercise at home in the wrong way, but once you get started you may find exercise tapes or videos are a helpful way of inspiring you to keep up the good work between classes. Don't overdo it to begin with, you will feel very stiff next day and are more likely to give up. Approach your exercise in the same way as you are now approaching your eating: reasonable, regular amounts (of food and exercise) are the way to keep your body well balanced.

It is very easy to convince yourself that you are 'too busy' to fit in exercise classes. If you work in a town there is likely to be a lunchtime class near you, and if you have young children there is usually a class with a crèche. Most sports centres have classes during the evenings or weekends. When did you last spend an hour watching television? You could have spent that hour much more profitably doing some exercise.

It can also be difficult for people who are overweight to go to an exercise class; they are afraid they will be stared at or laughed at. You don't have to squeeze into a skimpy leotard - wear something loose and comfortable. Or take up swimming, choosing a time when the pool is not likely to be busy. Water aerobics (also known as 'aquarobics') classes are also growing in popularity. The classes are held in the swimming pool (so nobody can see your legs), there are no mirrors, and the water stops you overheating. And don't forget about walking: to begin with you may just prefer a good brisk walk to build up your stamina.

Many compulsive eaters have an obsession about being slim, but the sort of slimness that is manufactured artificially from starvation, slimming pills and cosmetics has little to do with the slim body that comes with being fit and healthy. This is what you must aim for by following the Eating Plan and sorting out your stressful life problems. Exercise is an important part of achieving this.

LOW BLOOD SUGAR

Many compulsive eaters are amazed to be told that they have a low blood sugar problem, especially when they frequently binge on sweet, sugary carbohydrates.

Figure 2 shows what happens when a 'normal' meal is eaten. Carbohydrate and some of the protein is converted into *glucose*, which enters the bloodstream (A). The brain needs a minimum amount of blood-glucose to function properly (normal fasting level = the dotted line) and as the level rises (B) some of the glucose is burned by our muscles for energy. The pancreas produces insulin in moderate amounts to take the rest of the glucose out of the blood and store it in the liver as glycogen.

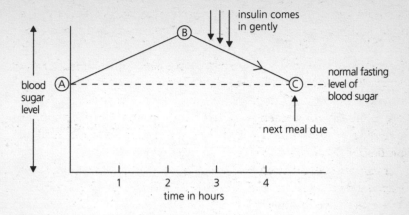

Figure 2 *What happens in a normal person*

The blood sugar level gradually falls until the next meal is due. When the blood sugar level returns to 'fasting level' (C) the brain becomes a little distressed and does three things:

1. It tries to get more glucose by increasing blood flow to the brain (making us feel a little cold as the blood rushes from our extremities to the brain).
2. It sends a message for adrenalin to be released. This pulls sugar out of its store in the liver (we feel cross, anxious and nervous and may get palpitations).
3. It stimulates the hunger centres (we feel hungry).

The picture is different, however, when the body is overloaded with glucose-rich foods such as bread, sweets, cake, biscuits and other refined carbohydrate. The level of sugar in the blood rises very quickly, which may give a 'high'. The pancreas has to produce *abnormally large* quantities of insulin to cope in a very short time. It is this large amount of insulin that causes blood sugar levels to fall rapidly to well below 'normal fasting level' as shown in Figure 3.

At this point the brain is being starved of glucose and there will be a craving for sweet food. There will also be other strong symptoms including palpitations, cold, confusion, nerves and depression.

If you binge at this point you will start the whole cycle again.

If you have been bingeing regularly you have been asking your pancreas to produce insulin too quickly and in abnormal quantities.

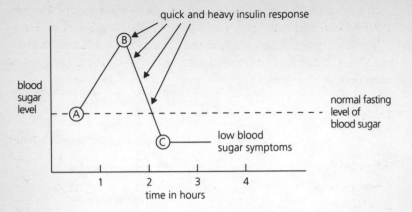

Figure 3

You have made the pancreas *sensitive*. Eating only one sweet can trigger a large insulin response which causes blood sugar to drop and you will find yourself craving food later in the day (see Figure 4).

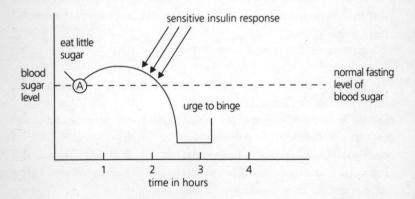

Figure 4

Fortunately a period of sensible eating (such as following the Maisner Eating Plan) can calm down an over-sensitive insulin response.

If you suffer frequently from more than 5 of the symptoms listed in Table 4, this may be because your blood sugar level drops too low at times.

Table 4

	Frequently	Sometimes	Never
Headaches	☐	☐	☐
Migraines	☐	☐	☐
Overweight	☐	☐	☐
Food cravings	☐	☐	☐
Forgetfulness	☐	☐	☐
Pre-menstrual tension	☐	☐	☐
Poor concentration	☐	☐	☐
Fainting fits	☐	☐	☐
Irritability	☐	☐	☐
Depression	☐	☐	☐
Nightmares	☐	☐	☐
Sleeplessness	☐	☐	☐
Vertigo	☐	☐	☐
Fatigue	☐	☐	☐
Anxiety	☐	☐	☐
Allergies	☐	☐	☐
Rapid heart beat	☐	☐	☐
Sweating	☐	☐	☐
Lack of co-ordination	☐	☐	☐
Emotional instability	☐	☐	☐
Confusion	☐	☐	☐
Panic attacks	☐	☐	☐
Exhaustion	☐	☐	☐
Cold sweats	☐	☐	☐
Frequent nightmares	☐	☐	☐
Unreasonable tiredness	☐	☐	☐
Tiredness around 3–4p.m.	☐	☐	☐

These symptoms may of course be due to other causes, but they can all point to low blood sugar levels. The most significant clue is attacks of tiredness and food cravings around mid-morning and extreme fatigue or even faintness mid-afternoon. The symptoms are relieved by eating something sweet, however this is *not* the best way to handle them, except as a test.

So how can dieting lead to compulsive eating? Many people become compulsive eaters after a period of successful dieting, or after trying and failing in many diets.

Few people diet properly. Most people semi-starve, losing large amounts of muscle tissue as well as water (as described earlier in this chapter). Their metabolism slows down and they feel psychologically deprived.

Quite simply, even if you are getting enough vitamins and minerals it is likely that your blood sugar is below crisis level for long periods of time (see Figure 5). This creates 'beyond hunger' cravings (a perfectly natural response) and binges become inevitable.

In other words . . .fast-loss diets slow you down and make you binge. It is also certain that any weight lost will be regained.

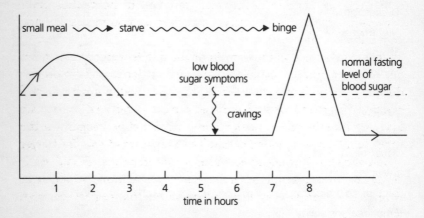

Figure 5

SUGAR CRAVINGS

Up until the start of the twentieth century sugar was a luxury, something the poor never expected to taste and out of the reach of the average consumer except as an occasional treat. Although people in previous centuries tended to consume more calories per person than we do now, they took them in the form of more nourishing foods rather than the kind of 'junk' food we have today. Also they were in general more physically active in the days before washing machines and motor cars.

Perhaps it was the luxury image of sugar that gave rise to the myth 'sugar is good for you.' This line is still being promoted by sweet manufacturers even though most people now know that sugar is made up of 'empty calories' and has no real nutritional value. We all know sugar leads to tooth decay, but there is less understanding among the general public of how large helpings of refined sugar disturb the body's natural energy balance.

It has been suggested that if refined sugar had not yet been discovered and someone were to try and introduce it onto the market today, it would be banned because of its bad effects on the human body.

Someone who derives a large part of his calorie intake each day from sugar - not just snacks of sweets and sticky buns but hidden sugars in breakfast cereals and processed foods - may in fact be suffering from malnutrition, which can lead to headaches, poor concentration and a variety of other symptoms, including compulsive eating.

There is a general confusion about the difference between starch and sugar, as both are classed as carbohydrate foods and are broken down by the body into fuel needed to power bodily functions and activities. Starch foods such as bread can act as carriers, so they are likely to contain other nutrients and fibre. Refined sugar, on the other hand, has no hidden extras. The only form of *unrefined* sugar would be a chunk of sugar beet or sugar cane in its 'just-picked' state. To extract the sugar for general use involves refining, so all sugar is refined - there is very little difference in this respect between white sugar and brown.

Unrefined or natural sugars contained in high-fibre food such as fruit are received by the body in a different way that is much gentler on the system. Instead of providing a sudden boost of neat energy which the body finds hard to handle, eating an apple (along with some protein) introduces the fruit sugar slowly into the system, giving the body a much better chance to handle it properly.

BODY RHYTHMS

The compulsive eater loses the ability to discern exactly what is going on in her body, so whenever something does not feel right she eats. Her sleep rhythms can often become disrupted, particularly if her life in general is chaotic. She may feel the frequent urge to eat in the middle of the night. One of the many reasons why nurses so often suffer from eating disorders is the unsociable hours they have to work, with night duty putting their body clocks out of balance.

If your life-style demands that you keep certain hours, you need to adjust your eating habits accordingly. If you have small children who start their day very early try not to stay up late at night, make sure you get sufficient sleep, and never skip breakfast even if it means you are eating it before dawn.

On the other hand, you may have a job that involves working late in the evening, in which case you should try and ensure you are not disturbed too early in the morning and that you plan your meals to give you regular nourishment during your waking hours.

Consider at what time of day you most crave food and time your main meal of the day to coincide with this. If you suffer real pangs at midday try to arrange that you take an early lunch break. This way you can eat properly when you need to rather than being tempted to nibble on an unsuitable snack until the official lunch hour comes round.

NIGHT EATING

If you know you always get a desire to eat at 2 a.m., prepare a sensible nourishing snack during the evening and leave it ready so you do not raid the larder for anything you can find. Don't tell yourself stories you don't believe about how you are not going to wake up and eat tonight, be realistic and accept this is how your body is reacting at present. When your system has become more stable you may well find the urge for a midnight feast naturally disappears. There are two main causes of night eating. One is nothing more mysterious than hunger. If you have not eaten enough during the day, the demands of your stomach will prevent you sleeping peacefully during the night. The other cause is depression. If you are constantly waking up when you know you have eaten enough, you should seek further help.

RELAXATION

If you have got into the habit of pepping up your system with coffee, cigarettes, alcohol and/or chocolate, your natural rhythms will be confused and you will be completely out of touch with the way your body works. Following the Eating Plan will help you rediscover this lost knowledge. Setting aside a short time each day for complete relaxation and deep breathing will also be beneficial.

Sit comfortably or lie flat on your back with your head supported by a cushion and concentrate on breathing slowly in and out. Explore how your body is feeling, imagine you are taking a journey through your body feeling the air entering your lungs, the blood being pumped around your arteries and veins and your muscles relaxing. In this way you learn to tune in to yourself.

MONTHLY CYCLE

The days before a period are often a difficult time for the compulsive eater, and cravings for certain foods are sometimes much more apparent. Nearly every woman whether she has eating problems or not gets a craving for sweet foods just before her period. This is so common it can almost be considered normal.

To help you become more aware of your individual pattern, complete Table 5 - marking a cross in the appropriate box each time you crave food which is unplanned, whether you actually eat it or not. The numbers at the top of the chart indicate the days in your cycle, with day 1 as the first day of your period, etc. Keep this record for at least three months; when it is complete it will be easy to see whether your food cravings are in fact related to your monthly cycle.

Armed with this knowledge about when you are likely to be feeling tense and when cravings are likely to hit you, you can be prepared. Allow yourself to eat a bit more at this time, being extra careful to avoid sugary and refined foods. It is believed that all women *need* about 500 extra calories a day prior to a period. You should therefore eat more frequently at this time and consider

Table 5 FOOD CRAVINGS IN RELATION TO THE MENSTRUAL CYCLE

	1	2	3	4	5	6	7	8	9	10	11	12	13	14	15	16	17	18	19	20	21	22	23	24	25	26	27	28
1st Month																												
2nd Month																												
3rd Month																												

	1	2	3	4	5	6	7	8	9	10	11	12	13	14	15	16	17	18	19	20	21	22	23	24	25	26	27	28
1st Month	×					×											×			×			×		×	×	× ×	× ×
2nd Month											×										×			×	×	× ×	× ×	×
3rd Month									×									×	×	×		×			× ×	×	×	×

taking vitamin supplements. Try not to plan stressful meetings or difficult jobs for this time, but make a note to give yourself a special treat like a visit to the hairdresser.

BACK IN CONTROL

To get back in control of your eating your body has to be re-educated, it has to learn that it is going to be fed regularly with nourishing food and that it does not have to stock up for a famine or prepare for a deluge. This is why the Eating Plan has been devised to include regular meals with snacks in between and contains plenty of protein, adequate unrefined carbohydrate and essential nutrition. Every time you cheat by skipping a meal or wandering from the rules you are undermining this education process and delaying your journey towards getting your eating under control.

5 The Maisner Eating Plan

The first thing to understand about this Eating Plan is that it is *not* a calorie-counting diet. A fanatical concern with counting calories is one of the causes of compulsive eating, because it leads to an obsession with the details of eating instead of encouraging you to focus on the overall picture of a balanced diet. By following the Eating Plan you will be eating well without taking in a great number of calories, so just forget your obsession with calories. To begin with don't worry about the quantities you are eating, but eat slowly and strictly according to the Plan, listening to your own body so that in time you will discover exactly what amounts are right for you. In this way good eating habits are developed and become an automatic way of life, even though it might take quite some time to achieve this.

The whole concept behind the Eating Plan is to develop a natural understanding of what your own body needs – this is the basic secret of getting your eating under control. For the first month in particular you must forget about trying to reduce your weight and concentrate on getting your eating habits under control. Many compulsive eaters do not realize that by careful choice of food it is possible to have a balanced diet, eat a good quantity of food and not feel hungry. Although many compulsive eaters and most bulimics do not recognize signs of hunger, there are other compulsive eaters who panic and feel guilty if they do not feel hungry all the time, assuming they must have been overeating. This anxiety will diminish as you develop a well-adjusted attitude towards food.

By the end of the first month you should be feeling more in control, more energetic and less lethargic, though exactly how long it takes for the benefits to be felt can vary widely from one person to the next. But around this time you should find that your cravings disappear and it will be easier to start exercising regularly. Weight reduction then becomes easier and you should gradually begin to lose weight, although with the increased feeling of well-being that sticking faithfully to the regime brings you will probably panic less about your weight as other things in life become more important. *The only really safe and permanent way to lose weight is to reform your eating habits, to take in fewer unnecessary calories while still making sure of adequate nutrition.*

Following this Eating Plan usually has one of two effects. You may feel terrific as soon as you start. Alternatively, you may feel tired as your body adjusts from a diet of high sugar, starch and caffeine to one of balanced amounts of protein, carbohydrate and essential vitamins and minerals. If you fall into the second group it is because your body is temporarily missing the instant energy effects of these substances, so for the first seven days it is probably advisable to eat more frequently than suggested.

The Eating Plan is well-balanced and will benefit everyone, eating problem or not. It can be used as a basis for family meals, but if your family flatly refuses to give up chips and puddings, accept the fact and cater accordingly.

If you are following a diet prescribed by your doctor for specific medical reasons other than eating problems you should consult with him or her before embarking on this Eating Plan. If you have any known allergies or know that certain foods cause you medical problems, don't eat those foods under any circumstances. There are substitutes listed.

Protein foods are a very important part of the Eating Plan. Protein is the body-builder that repairs tissues and satisfies hunger, and although it is essential for good health it is often avoided by compulsive eaters. The main sources of protein are animal products such as meat, fish, eggs and cheese, but there are also vegetable proteins for those who prefer to follow a vegetarian diet. The following list shows a good range of protein foods that are all excellent for including in the Eating Plan, unless you know something is one of your trigger foods, in which case it should be avoided.

- Meat: all kinds (remove excess fat)
- Fish: all kinds
- Cheese: any is suitable
- Eggs
- Milk, including milk products such as cheese, yogurt, fromage frais

- TVP Meat Substitute and products made from it such as meatless burgers
- Tofu and products made from it such as tofu burgers
- Pulses such as lentils and beans
- Nuts
- Quorn and products made from it

Based around this choice of protein foods you can now build up for yourself an eating plan that will include a meal or snack at least every three to four hours. As you get back in touch with your natural feelings of hunger you should arrange your eating style to suit your body's individual needs. For example, if you find you tend to feel hungrier in the early part of the day, you could style your eating plan to include two 'breakfasts'. To begin with, however, you can stick to the regime of every three to four hours and try to ensure that each meal or snack, especially breakfast, includes some protein.

Plenty of fruit and vegetables are needed as well, and also unrefined carbohydrate foods for slow-release energy during the day. These include

- Bread
- Rice
- Pasta
- Potatoes

Always choose whole grains (wholemeal bread, brown rice). The best way to eat potatoes is baked in their jackets for full nutritional value and fibre.

Yogurt, fruit and cheese make handy snacks. Plan ahead to make sure you always have something available and are never tempted to miss even one snack. Include small amounts of polyunsaturated fats such as olive oil, and also eat blue fish such as trout and sardines. But as fat is so high in calories the amount included daily should be limited. (Please refer to the Appendix.)

No coffee or alcohol is allowed, and *no refined sugars*. This is usually the part of the plan that people find it hardest to get used to, but once you have loosened the grip that these artificial stimulants have on your system you will begin to feel very much better. Remember that this exclusion is not necessarily forever; once you are firmly back in control of your eating again you will be able to include these substances. By then they should be something you want to enjoy only occasionally; you will no longer suffer dreadful cravings for them.

When it comes to drinks try and develop a taste for spring water, which is excellent for everyone's health. If you want something with more flavour try experimenting with the broad range of herb and fruit teas now widely on sale in supermarkets and health shops. Most of the best-known brands of fizzy drinks are made in sugar-free versions, and there are also caffeine- and sugar-free varieties of cola that fit in with the guidelines of the Eating Plan. Fresh fruit juice, Bovril and milk are all suitable, while decaffeinated coffee and tea can replace the usual caffeine-loaded forms of these beverages.

The Eating Plan gives you free choice in planning your meals. There is no list of items you must have at every meal, nor are you expected to follow the Plan to the letter, *although the strict rule about timing meals - eating at least every three to four hours - must be adhered to*. The whole point of the Plan is to teach you to devise your own menus, following the Plan's guidelines, so that you will learn good eating habits for life.

However, to get you started here are a few sample menus (Tables 6 - 10) to suit different tastes and different occasions. You may also like to look at Table 13 in Chapter 7 and compare the eating habits of Claire and Jane while Claire was following the Eating Plan.

Note: All those who are on special diets, especially diabetics, must consult with their doctor before embarking on any of these eating plans.

Table 6 THE MAISNER METHOD BASIC EATING PLAN

On Rising:	Orange juice
Breakfast:	A portion of protein and/or porridge or shredded wheat. One slice of wholemeal bread or toast, if tolerated, with low-fat spread
Mid-morning Snack:	A portion of protein, with fruit if desired
Lunch:	A portion of protein, vegetables and either a jacket potato, wholemeal pasta or brown rice. Fruit or yogurt
Afternoon Snack:	Protein snack

Dinner: One meat or 'substitute' e.g. egg, cheese, fish, TVP, Quorn, pulses or beans. Salad and vegetables or jacket potato.

About Four   Protein snack
Hours Later:

Table 7 EXAMPLE OF A DAY'S EATING

On Rising: Orange juice

Breakfast: Eggs, bacon and tomatoes

Mid-morning   Yogurt and apple
Snack:

Lunch: Tinned tuna fish in brine with coleslaw and beetroot

Afternoon   Cottage cheese and fresh fruit
Snack:

Dinner: a) Home-made soup
                 b) Chicken, broccoli heads, mixed salad and baked potato
                 c) Tinned fruit packed in water

About Four   Skimmed milk drink with vanilla essence
Hours Later:

Table 8 EXAMPLE OF A DAY'S EATING FOR A VEGETARIAN

On Rising: Orange juice

Breakfast: Natural yogurt with sunflower and sesame seeds

Mid-morning   Celery and tahini dip
Snack:

Lunch: Cheese on toast with a mixed salad

Afternoon   Cottage cheese and fresh fruit
Snack:

Dinner: a) Lentil and vegetable soup
                 b) Mushroom omelette, spinach, dash soya, baked potato
                 c) Tinned fruit packed in water

About Four   Skimmed milk drink with vanilla essence
Hours Later:

NB. All those on special medical diets, especially diabetics, must consult with their doctor before embarking on any of these eating plans.

Table 9 EXAMPLE OF A DAY'S EATING FOR A VEGAN

On Rising: Orange juice

Breakfast: Soya sausages, mushrooms and wholemeal toast

Mid-morning Vegan cheese on rice cakes
Snack:

Lunch: Tofu burger, tomato, onion, lettuce, rice salad, fruit

Afternoon Soya yogurt with roasted sunflower seeds
Snack:

Dinner: a) Vegetable soup
  b) Chilli con carne with kidney beans and TVP, sweetcorn
     and pepper salad
  c) Fresh fruit

About Four Rice cake and lentil pâté
Hours Later:

Table 10 THE AIROLA DIET
(Low Animal Protein – High Natural Carbohydrate)

The American author Dr Paavo Airola evolved a diet that contains (in order of importance):

1. Grains, seeds and nuts
2. Vegetables
3. Fruit

This diet is low in animal sources of protein but high in the protein from grains, seeds and nuts.

Dr Airola believes that raw and sprouted grains and seeds should be the main protein source, animal proteins being kept to a minimum. All seeds and nuts are eaten fresh and raw. Cereals are permitted provided they are eaten in their 'whole' state and not refined. Millet is especially recommended. He recommends that meat be eaten only on a weekly basis, if at all. The diet is as follows:

7 a.m. Glass of fruit juice. Sweet juice must be diluted with water 50/50.

8 a.m. Breakfast. Nuts, seeds, fruit, yogurt, cottage cheese, OR, Cooked cereal with oil and raw milk.

10 a.m. Snack — a few nuts OR a glass of yogurt OR a piece of fruit.

12 noon Glass of fresh juice.

1 p.m.	Lunch. Cooked cereal, e.g. buckwheat, millet, etc., with oil and milk (if not eaten for breakfast), OR, fruit or vegetable salad with yogurt and 2 slices of wholewheat bread with cheese and butter.
3 p.m.	Glass of juice with 2 tablespoonsful of yeast added.
5 p.m.	Glass of fresh vegetable juice.
6 p.m.	Dinner. Vegetable salad with cooked vegetable dish of: beans, tortillas, yams, green beans, baked potatoes etc. Slice or two of wholewheat bread. Cottage cheese, yogurt. Animal protein if desired.
8 p.m.	Glass of milk or yogurt with 1 or 2 tablespoonsful of Brewer's yeast.

By now you should be feeling inspired to get started on your own eating plan, but before you begin it is essential that you read, understand and memorize the following ten-point list of rules. These rules contain the secret of success; follow them without faltering and you cannot go wrong. Before long your eating will be back under your control. But remember, if you do slip up ~ and everyone does from time to time because we are human beings and not machines ~ it is not the end of the world. Don't feel guilty, just start again with renewed determination. The longer you stick to the Plan the easier it gets because your body begins to work with you instead of fighting against you. As your body chemistry becomes steadier the dreadful cravings and urges to eat disappear ~ but only if you stick to the 10 rules.

TEN STEPS TO EATING CONTROL

These guidelines have worked for others and will work for you.

1. NEVER GO LONGER THAN THREE TO FOUR HOURS DURING THE DAY WITHOUT EATING

Little and often is the golden rule when it comes to controlling your eating habits. This does not mean life becomes one long nibble, in fact regular protein meals will help eliminate the desire to pick between meals as well as the urge to binge. Bulimics in particular, who cannot cope with the sensation of a full stomach, should ensure they have at least six small meals a day. The main benefit of this system is that it stabilizes your blood sugar levels. This will make you feel much more in control of how your body is functioning.

Each meal and each snack should contain some protein and some carbohydrate. This may sound daunting at first, but by consulting the protein list again (page 67) you will see that you needn't cook yourself a piece of fish or grill a chicken six times a day – a handy snack of cheese and fruit can be carried with you wherever you go.

Anyone used to dieting is likely to react with horror to being asked to eat every three or four hours, but remember these meals need not be large because they are nutritious. The Eating Plan will get your eating back under control because semi-starvation diets have helped cause it to slip out of control. Remember that, although you may think you are eating more at first, you will find you are no longer bingeing on high-calorie foods.

Have a look at Claire and Jane in Chapter 7 to see how, in practice, eating more meals of better quality actually works out at less calories in the long run.

People on a low income may be worried they will not be able to afford to buy lots of protein foods. Remember you will be buying these foods instead of those cakes, sweets and biscuits, not in addition to them, and think how much you will save when you are no longer bingeing. Protein does not have to be expensive. Cheaper cuts of meat, tinned pilchards or beans and pulses provide good protein at low cost.

2. EAT BREAKFAST EVERY DAY

Blood sugar levels drop during the night and if they are not topped up at breakfast time they will fall alarmingly during the morning, creating an urge to binge. Sugary breakfast cereals are no good in controlling blood sugar levels. They just encourage the quick lift and consequential drop which leads to mid-morning sugar craving (see point 5, below). Study Table 11 to see just how much refined sugar is contained in your favourite packet cereals and which are safe to include in your eating plan.

Table 11

Product	Percentage of sugar
Coco Krispies	43
Sugar Frosted Flakes	41
Frosted Rice	37
Honey Nut Loops	35
Coco Puffs	33.3
Raisin Bran	29
Frosted Mini-wheats	26
100% Bran	21
All Bran	19
Grape Nuts Flakes	13.3
40% Bran Flakes	13
Rice Krispies	7.8
Grape-Nuts	7
Special K	5.4
Corn Flakes	5.3
Weetabix	5.2
Shredded Wheat	0.6
Puffed Wheat	0.5
Puffed Rice	0.1

Protein for breakfast, on the other hand, accompanied by some unrefined carbohydrate will keep blood sugar levels steady for hours, certainly until your next snack is due. You will also find it much easier to get through the day with a good protein start. Porridge is the only non-protein exception to this rule: provided oats are not a trigger food, porridge has the ability to stabilize blood sugar levels and makes a good breakfast (but not with added sugar!)

An ideal breakfast on the Eating Plan might be grapefruit, poached egg on wholemeal toast with a slice of ham and a cup of herb tea. Although this is fine at the weekends, many people find it difficult to go to the trouble of cooking before they dash off to work. You can eat a tub of cottage cheese and an apple without opening your eyes, or prepare a plate of ham and hard-boiled eggs the night before and leave it in the fridge or packed in a plastic box so you can take it with you to eat in the car.

Too many people, whether they have an eating disorder or not, complain that they cannot face eating first thing in the morning. This is often due to generally bad eating habits, perhaps eating too much late at night, low blood sugar levels or feeling too tired and rushed in the mornings. If this is your excuse you have got to work at overcoming it because *your eating will never be under control as long as your blood sugar levels are unstable.* To make the Eating Plan work for you, you have to commit yourself to eating breakfast – if possible a protein breakfast – every single day.

3. EAT PROTEIN AT EVERY MEAL

Protein is used in the production and repair of skin, hair, nails and blood, as well as hormones, digestive juices, mucus and phlegm. If this essential material is not supplied your body will 'borrow' it from muscle tissue, leading to flabbiness. High-protein diets also satisfy your hunger better: just consider whether you feel more satisfied after a seven-ounce steak or after seven ounces of doughnuts. Table 24 in the Appendix is a comprehensive list of foods showing their protein content; this should help you plan your menus (the calorie contents are included to help you calculate which foods give the best protein per calorie value). Aim to include around 90 g of protein each day.

Although protein is essential for a healthy diet, particularly for anyone with an eating disorder, many compulsive eaters avoid it out of the mistaken idea that it is 'fattening'. Protein is a complex food structure that is digested slowly and is therefore introduced into the body gradually over a long period of time – exactly what is needed to re-educate your body to expect regular food. This slow release of fuel cuts down on the urge to binge because your body feels well nourished and is not constantly demanding to be fed. Without the binges, your overall calorie consumption is also reduced.

One of the reasons why changing to a vegetarian diet can lead to bingeing is that protein levels may be drastically reduced. The most obvious protein sources are animal products, but there are plenty of good sources of vegetable protein, essential for a healthy vegetarian diet.

The majority of vegetarians are happy to include products that come from animals but do not involve the animal being killed, such as milk and eggs. Vegans, however, avoid even these animal-based items and need to work very hard at ensuring they have a well-balanced diet that includes complete protein. (See Table 10, page 71.)

Protein is made up of different amino acids, and while all these amino acids are found in meat and fish only certain ones appear in some vegetarian foods, so careful food combining is necessary to build up complete protein. Figure 6 explains this.

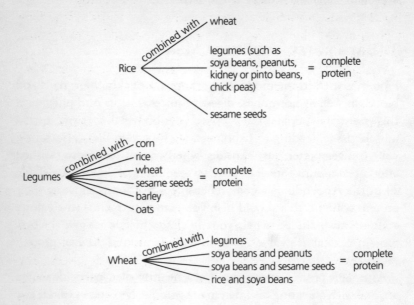

Figure 6

If you are dedicated to a vegan diet it is advisable to get specialist advice from a nutritionist to ensure you are getting sufficient protein and adequate amounts of vitamin B_{12}, vitamin D and calcium. Also check that the soya milk you buy has added vitamin D and calcium.

4. AVOID ALL CONCENTRATED SUGARS

Although it is true that your body needs 'sugar' as its fuel (everything you eat eventually turns into glucose, the fuel your body's energy system runs on), the sugar your body needs is not the kind that comes in sweets, chocolate, cake or refined in a bag. There is plenty of sugar available from the breakdown of other foods, for example:

Carbohydrates: convert into 100 per cent sugar
Fats: convert into 10 per cent sugar
Protein: converts into 50 per cent sugar

Starchy unrefined carbohydrate foods such as baked potatoes and fruit can supply all the body's 'sugar' needs to refuel, provided these healthy foods are eaten in regular quantities. Along with sugar these foods provide fibre (to keep the gut healthy) and vitamins and minerals, are essential to good health.

The fact that the human race – and animal life in general – has survived for thousands of years without refined sugar proves how unnecessary it is.

The problem is that sugar tastes so nice, chocolate can so easily become an addiction and you have probably been hooked since you were a small child. Taste-buds do change, however, if they are re-educated. If you are used to eating a lot of refined sugar foods and try to cut them out suddenly, so you have to be prepared to miss them at first.

Start by keeping temptation at bay: don't buy biscuits, cakes and sweets. If they are in the house you are likely to eat them. To begin with allow yourself extra portions of sweet fruit alongside your protein (but take care: too much sweet fruit alone may trigger a binge). This will appease your sugar craving but you will be taking the sugar in a far healthier form.

After a while, as your blood sugar levels stabilize, your craving for sugar will subside. It is a well-known fact, however, that many women crave sugar around the time of their period. Be prepared for these ups and downs and don't feel you are failing if your sweet tooth rebels from time to time. As your taste-buds change you will soon find this is no longer a major problem.

Concentrated sugars are generally things that end in '-ose' such as fructose, dextrose or sucrose, so even if a product says it is 'sugar-free' make sure it does not contain any of these other, hidden sugars, which are equally unsuitable on the Eating Plan. (For a list of the hidden sugars in certain foods, see Table 25 in the Appendix.)

5. DO NOT EAT BREAKFAST CEREALS

As Table 11 (page 74) shows, breakfast cereals contain a lot of hidden sugar. A bowl of cereal is a quick energy-boosting snack at any time of the day or night, but for compulsive eaters it is double trouble.

Firstly, the high amount of refined sugar plays havoc with your blood sugar levels. Secondly, cereal itself often triggers a binge. Lengthy experience with compulsive eaters and bulimics has shown that a great of many of them cannot handle cereal – even one bowl of cornflakes or a slice of bread is the thing that sparks off a massive binge. These cereals have to be avoided and replaced by protein and non-cereal carbohydrate foods. Once again the emphasis is on the importance of a protein breakfast. However, if cereal is not a trigger then natural porridge can be included for breakfast if you like.

6. Choose Whole Grains

Unless they are trigger foods, bread, rice and pasta can be included in the Eating Plan. Always choose whole grain varieties to ensure you are getting maximum nutrition for your calories. Wholemeal bread and brown rice are also far more satisfying than the refined varieties. This will help in your battle to beat the urge to binge, as well as providing extra fibre, vitamins and nutrients. Like any other part of the body, the digestive organs will become flabby and inefficient if they are not made to work. Eating plenty of fibre will tone up your whole system. Refined and processed foods have had most of their fibre removed, which makes them easy to eat but not particularly healthy to digest. By including whole grains in your daily diet as well as other fibre-providers such as fresh fruit and vegetables you will feel healthier and keep disease at bay while getting your eating under control.

7. No Alcohol

This is a very important rule and should be obeyed absolutely for at least the first few weeks of the Eating Plan. If you feel panicky at the idea of not being able to drink you should take a careful look at your drinking habits and consider whether you have a drink problem as well as an eating problem. It is not unusual for the two to go together; both arise as a result of life problems and not being in control. Whether this is expressed through binge eating, excess alcohol intake, drug addiction or a combination of these, the basic deep-rooted problem is the same. Much of what is written in this book to help compulsive eaters can be applied equally well to those with a drink problem. Following the Eating Plan will also help you fight alcohol addiction, but you may well need additional professional help. If you get your eating under control but still have a drink problem, you have not really beaten your life problems, so the two must be worked on together.

Others find it difficult to give up drinking because of social factors. Yet this need not be a problem: there is a wide range of non-alcoholic drinks available and drink-drive laws make it quite socially acceptable to refuse alcohol.

It is often not the amount of alcohol drunk that matters. Some people can find just two glasses of wine triggers off a binge. Alcohol has a worse effect than refined sugar on blood sugar levels, so you are undoing a lot of good work if you avoid sugar but drink alcohol. Alcohol is high in calories and when under the influence of drink your level of self-control is lowered so it is easier to slip out of good habits or start bingeing. The best way to stay in control is to cut out alcohol absolutely at first.

8. CUT OUT CAFFEINE

Again, many people panic when told to stop drinking coffee or cola. As little as three or four cups of coffee a day can make you psychologically and physically dependent on caffeine. As with any other addiction, it is easy to slip into and hard to kick.

If you are in the habit of taking a lot of coffee and decide to give up suddenly you might feel really bad for about four days. Withdrawal symptoms can include headaches, lethargy, irritability, panic attacks, inability to work, severe depression, jitters and extreme drowsiness. If possible, quit the caffeine habit at a time when you are not under particular pressure. You may find it easier to cut down gradually over a number of days, replacing as many cups of coffee as possible with herb tea, cereal-based substitutes or one of the caffeine-free teas or coffees sold in shops (as long as cereal is not a trigger). Mix your caffeinated coffee half and half with decaffeinated, gradually reducing the proportion of caffeinated coffee over several days until you find you can cope with being caffeine-free.

You must also keep in mind that caffeine is not just found in coffee (as Table 12 shows). Check labels to make sure you are buying caffeine-free foods and beverages.

Table 12

Chocolate bar	160 mg per 8 oz (225 g)
Aspirin-based tablets	15–30 mg each
Coffee	100–150 mg per cupful
Tea	60–75 mg per cupful
Cola drinks	40–60 mg per cupful

Caffeine is similar to refined sugar in that it raises blood sugar levels, but it does this by stimulating the adrenal glands. As the Eating Plan is aimed at levelling off blood sugar and eliminating the peaks and troughs that lead to bingeing, caffeine must be avoided.

Slimmers often believe that caffeine is 'slimming' because it can raise the metabolic rate and burn off more calories. This is another of those beliefs which, although true in principle, does not work in practice. Caffeine triggers the release of insulin, which causes hunger and sugar craving and is likely to lead to extra eating. It is also a diuretic, which causes thirst. As many compulsive eaters cannot differentiate between thirst and hunger they are again likely to eat more if they are taking caffeine.

Cutting out caffeine is essential while following the Eating Plan, especially in the first few weeks. Don't think that all this means you are under a life sentence never to drink coffee again, or never to eat another chocolate in your life. Once your eating is under control you will probably be able to enjoy these things from time to time, although most people find they choose not to. The difference will be that you will no longer fear them or suffer uncontrollable desires for them. You will be making the choice about whether you include them in your life or not.

9. DON'T COUNT CALORIES

The Eating Plan is designed to turn you into a normal eater. It makes no claims that you will lose five pounds a week, flatten your stomach or firm up your thighs – although you can make all these things come about once you are back in control of your eating habits. You have probably been dieting and counting calories for a number of years without success, otherwise you would not have an eating disorder, so you have nothing to lose by trying a new approach.

While kicking the calorie-counting habit you must also stop weighing yourself. Weighing yourself several times a day or even several times a week can lead to a binge if you find you have gone up a pound or two. Instead, tune in to your body: how does it feel? What does it need? If you are tired have an early night, if you are hungry increase the quantity of nourishing food you are eating, if you are full don't finish everything that is on your plate. Try to listen to what your body is telling you. It is a much more reliable guide to good health than the scales or counting calories.

10. Enjoy the Eating Plan!

The Eating Plan is a great adventure. It is the path that is going to lead you out of your disastrous eating habits and back to being in control of your eating and enjoying your life. *It will work for you*; plunge in with enthusiasm. A positive attitude towards the plan could make all the difference between sticking with it until you see results or giving up at the first hurdle. Never feel as if you are punishing yourself by placing restrictions on your eating habits. Never feel deprived and ill-used because you are forbidden your 'favourite' food and drink. Get into the habit of telling yourself that you are *choosing* not to eat these foods because they are bad for you. Say:

'I love and respect myself too much to damage my health and well-being.'

There are a few people who adopt the Eating Plan and never waver from it, quickly discovering how it is transforming their lives and rapidly getting their eating back under control. These are the lucky ones, or perhaps they did not have too serious a problem to begin with. For the majority it is not that easy. Emotional problems crop up, unforeseen difficulties appear, the urge to binge becomes too strong to resist and all good intentions fly out of the window. Accept that it is quite possible this will happen to you at some point. You may do brilliantly for a week and then a crisis arises and everything seems to fall apart. Don't worry and don't feel guilty about showing a little human failing. Just appreciate that this is the very reason why you are working at getting your eating under control. Your aim is eventually to be able to handle a crisis without falling apart, so pick yourself up and start again until one day you succeed in breaking through to a new level of control.

As a quick reminder you may find it helpful to copy out the ten steps and pin the list up somewhere handy so you can refer to it whenever necessary. Here they are again, in brief:

1. Never go longer than three to four hours during the day without eating
2. Have breakfast every day
3. Include protein in every meal and snack
4. Cut out all refined and concentrated sugars
5. Avoid breakfast cereals
6. Choose whole grains and avoid refined foods
7. Do not drink alcohol
8. Cut out caffeine
9. Never count calories and don't weigh yourself
10. Enjoy following the Eating Plan.

3

Cause and Effect

6 The Triggers, Goodies and Baddies

Many compulsive eaters learn to recognize that there are certain foods that trigger a binge. One biscuit sets the whole thing in motion, bingers know they are not capable of eating just one. The trigger food has to be avoided like the enemy or eating slips out of control.

This is not the same as finding a food 'moreish'. Most people have experienced this: it's the feeling you get when you dip into a bowl of peanuts at a party and find you can't leave them alone until the bowl is empty. For the compulsive eater, however, one taste of a trigger food sets them off bingeing not just on that trigger food but on any and every food she can lay hands on.

This reaction accounts for much of the fear surrounding food and eating that haunts those with eating disorders. They know their vulnerabilities and life becomes a battle to avoid foods that will make them lose control.

A trigger food can often be something people don't even like, or something they knows disagrees with them. It is known that craving a food may be a sign of an allergy to it, so a cream cake may be craved by someone who has an allergy to dairy products ~ the logical mind says no but the craving is irresistible. Common trigger foods are refined cereals, white bread, cakes, pies, chocolates, sweets or dairy products. Triggers are rarely low-calorie, healthy items such as oranges or celery, although apples are known to be a trigger for some people and dried fruit is another frequent culprit.

RECOGNIZING TRIGGER FOODS

The most obvious sign of a trigger food is that once eaten it fuels the desire to binge on other foods and the inability to stop eating. But trigger foods can bring on other symptoms such as hot and cold sweats, bloating, rashes, headaches and tiredness and lethargy or hyperactivity and shaking hands.

All or any of these symptoms may also be caused by an allergy to a given food. A true allergy causes the body to produce antibodies that create physical symptoms – such as a rash from eating strawberries. These antibodies can be detected by skin tests. Many people also suffer from sensitivity to certain foods, which can also bring on symptoms without producing antibodies. Trigger foods may mimic the symptoms of a food allergy or sensitivity and, in turn, both food allergies and sensitivities can act as triggers.

ISOLATING TRIGGER FOODS

It is important to try to isolate your trigger foods. Although you may know one or some of your triggers – most people know they can't eat just one biscuit or just one chocolate – there may be others you are unaware of. Hot and cold sweats, especially during the night, invariably point to some sort of food intolerance. If you suffer from these check back on whether you have eaten a lot of a particular food, or something unusual, that day. Symptoms can go on for years without their true cause being discovered. If the problem arises in mid-life it is not unusual for a woman to be told her hot sweats are due to the menopause. She will accept this without associating them with having an eating problem.

Some doctors believe the cause of most migraines to be allergies to foods. Chocolate, sweets, alcohol and cheese can cause headaches, so if there appears to be no obvious medical reason for repeated headaches it is a good idea to check your eating habits.

Research at the Maisner Centre for Eating Disorders has shown that changing to the Centre's Eating Plan (see Chapter 5) with its balanced nutrition and emphasis on stabilizing blood sugar levels has, in many cases, resulted in the disappearance of some true allergies, including hay fever.

Muesli for breakfast may sound healthy but it could mean the start of a miserable day if one or more of the ingredients – cereal, raisins, milk – sets off deep-seated cravings to eat.

A coffee morning also has hidden dangers. Eating a single biscuit may spark off an uncontrollable urge to leave as soon as possible and go home to binge. The compulsive eater may have a sensitivity to the flour or sugar in the biscuit. Then, having had one biscuit, she feels guilty and her control snaps – having eaten one why not eat the lot? This leads to suddenly eating a lot of sweet biscuits, probably after eating very little in recent hours or days, and the consequent upset of blood sugar levels increases the urge to eat even more.

While someone who is not a compulsive eater yet who ate a lot of biscuits may think that she really should not have eaten so many but that they were too tasty to refuse, the compulsive eater may be miserable for days, bingeing and vomiting because she allowed herself to eat one biscuit.

Fast foods and instant meals may prove difficult to handle as well. Some artificial additives and colourings can act as triggers. It can be difficult isolating these triggers, as additives can differ from brand to brand and within different products in a range.

SEMI-TRIGGERS

Other foods can be 'semi-triggers'. Eaten now and again they are not a problem, but too much turns them into triggers.

Pat was getting her eating back under control, so one day she ate one biscuit. 'I'm OK, it isn't a problem,' she said. The next day she ate two biscuits, still convinced she could handle it. By the fifth day she ate a whole tin-full of biscuits and carried on into a full-scale binge. The build-up had pushed her over her level of tolerance.

SUBTLE CHANGES

Another problem with trigger foods is that they can change. You may know that bread is a trigger so you avoid bread and have porridge for breakfast each morning. This is fine for a while, then you realize that oats have become a trigger and it is the porridge that is setting you off. This may be due to your eating more oats than usual, perhaps when you only had the occasional portion of oats you could handle it, but porridge every day built up into a trigger. A new trigger may be the culprit if you suddenly get the urge to binge when you have not had any of your usual trigger foods.

KEEP YOUR DISTANCE

The only way to handle trigger foods successfully is to temporarily *avoid* them. Get to know what your triggers are, then tell yourself these are foods that you cannot allow yourself to eat. If, for example, you knew you had an allergy to shellfish and you came up in a terrible rash every time you ate it, you would avoid it and not feel embarrassed about telling people you were not able to eat it. Treat your trigger foods in exactly the same way. They are the things that make you 'ill'; if you want to stay healthy and happy you have to avoid them. When you are truly cured of your eating problems you should be able to eat these things again – if you still want to.

Try to avoid buying those foods you know to be your triggers. This is less difficult for those who live alone than those who have family to consider. There is no need to have sweets and biscuits in the house. If the children are old enough to make demands they are old enough to buy their own, and it will do them no harm to try to cut down their sugar intake. If bread is a problem perhaps the rest of the family could make their own sandwiches so you are not directly confronted with the loaf. Never feel guilty about expecting a bit of co-operation from those you share your life with.

HANDY SUBSTITUTES

If it is impossible to avoid a trigger food completely, have a substitute always handy so you can provide yourself with an alternative and not feel deprived.

Mark discovered that alcohol was his trigger; whenever he had a drink he went on to eat huge amounts. When he understood how this was wrecking his life he was determined to give up alcohol, but as he and his wife entertained a lot it was difficult to avoid it in the house. He made sure there were always fruit juices, soda water and soft drinks in the house, which made it much easier for him to steer away from alcohol.

THE GOODIES – WHAT YOUR BODY NEEDS

Disordered eating patterns often lead to fluctuations in the levels of vitamins and minerals in your body. Bulimics in particular can easily lose too many vital nutrients if they are making themselves sick and taking laxatives and diuretics. A balanced diet should contain healthy amounts of foods that are rich sources of vitamins and minerals (see Table 26 in the Appendix).

POTASSIUM

Potassium is a particularly important mineral. Every cell in the body needs potassium to function correctly. It is vital for maintaining correct fluid balances. Potassium levels drop severely after vomiting, which can lead to serious problems such as kidney failure, heart attacks and, in rare cases, epileptic fits. Low potassium levels also lead to sugar cravings, which in turn create bingeing, weight gain and the desire to purge the body further.

CHROMIUM AND MAGNESIUM

Although only minute quantities of chromium are needed by the body - about 5 g in an entire lifetime - it is of critical importance. It plays a crucial part in the action of insulin and the control of sugar metabolism. If there is a deficiency the result may be fluctuating energy levels, sugar cravings and worsening of premenstrual symptoms.

Chromium levels are usually high in babies and young children, but decrease as years go by, particularly if the diet includes a lot of sweet foods, which increase the excretion of chromium in the urine.

Magnesium is another vital mineral. If it is in short supply the body may react by craving a food containing magnesium - the most easily available of which is usually chocolate.

SALT

Eating foods high in salt can lead to a tendency for the body to retain fluid. How much this affects each individual depends on his own body chemistry, but in general we probably all eat too much salt. Even without sprinkling extra over a meal there is enough hidden salt in most foods to more than supply the body's needs.

Bacon, cheese, smoked fish, chutneys and bottled sauces, certain breakfast cereals and most processed foods have plenty of salt added before we buy them, not to mention obvious salt-laden snacks such as crisps and peanuts.

Without becoming obsessed with hidden salt, it is sensible to be more aware of how much salt you are taking in and to decide whether it is more than your body needs.

FATS

Fat is another substance that can be hidden in prepared foods. Although the body needs a certain amount of fat, our Western diet generally tends to be too fatty. This is disastrous for those who want to lose weight. Pound for pound, fat is the most fattening food there is.

Oil is also a fat and, although unsaturated oils such as olive oil are considered more beneficial to health than saturated ones, both contain equal calories.

Fried foods retain a lot of fat, so grill meat and bake rather than fry chips. Pastry and cakes are made with a high proportion of fat; mayonnaise is largely oil; nuts are another source of fat. Butter and cheese are perhaps most obviously fatty foods.

Avoiding fat is something that can easily become an obsession with people who are over-concerned about their weight. Some people feel compelled to wipe every bit of food in case there is fat to be removed, or feel frightened and threatened in the presence of food that might have fat in it. Not surprisingly, then, high-fat foods are often craved when bingeing. (For help with preparing your eating plan see Table 27 – 'Hidden Fats' – in the Appendix.)

THE BADDIES –
WHAT YOUR BODY DOESN'T NEED

CAFFEINE AND ALCOHOL

As mentioned in the ten-point plan in Chapter 5, caffeine and alcohol stimulate blood sugar levels artificially.

It has been proved over and over again that it is not possible to really get your eating under control while you are continuing to use caffeine and alcohol. Once you are back in control of your eating these things can be reintroduced gradually – hopefully by then you will no longer need them as constant props.

If you find you can't face the thought of giving up drinking alcohol, it is likely that you have a drink problem as well as an eating problem. Much of the advice given in this book for overcoming eating problems is equally valid for overcoming drink problems, including following the Eating Plan, but it is advised that you seek out professional help for your drinking as well.

CIGARETTES

Smoking uses up large quantities of essential nutrients, particularly vitamin C, just as drinking large amounts of alcohol, coffee or tea does. If at the same time your diet is lacking in essential foods, your body becomes depleted. When your body gets to this state not only do you feel under par but you are more open to illness – anything from colds to cancer. This applies to everyone who smokes but in particular to those whose diet is inadequate. Smoking can also boost sugar levels artificially, an added problem if you are trying to keep your eating controlled.

LAXATIVES

Being sick is not the only way a bulimic discovers of ridding her body of its overload of food. Laxatives rush food through the system so that – although calories are taken up – much of the food's nutrition is not absorbed. Laxative taking is a surprisingly easy habit to slip into.

Most people with an eating disorder suffer from constipation, mainly because they are not eating enough or are vomiting up what they have eaten so there is no bulk to make the intestines work efficiently. They also tend to lack sufficient body fluids. When these people binge it is too much for the body to cope with all at once, causing further problems.

The best way to overcome constipation is, of course, to return to a normal diet, but meanwhile a bulking agent such as *Fibrogel*, along with glycerine suppositories – both of which can be bought over the counter at the chemist – are helpful in the short term. Additional exercise can also improve the condition of the bowels and intestines.

A good diet will include adequate amounts of fibre. Table 28 in the Appendix is a guide to foods high in dietary fibre.

Taking laxatives when needed and using the recommended dose is not harmful. The problem always comes when they are taken to excess and you find yourself building up from several a day to an extreme amount.

Laxatives do not shift body fat, they merely rid the intestines of excess fluid and fibre, so on their own they are no way to lose fat. All you lose is essential nutrients, leading to malnutrition and debility.

The more laxatives are abused, the more they become needed because the intestinal muscles lose the ability to work by themselves, unaided. Abusing laxatives to try and achieve a flat stomach only has the opposite effect as they tend to make the abdomen blow out and look bigger. They also encourage hunger pangs to return more quickly than if the intestines had been allowed to empty naturally.

If laxative abuse is only a minor problem, gradually reduce the number taken until it is down to one or two a day. However, if the abuse is severe it is important to consult your doctor, as cutting down suddenly and drastically could cause serious problems. If you have a sympathetic doctor he or she may be able to recommend ways of getting your bowel movements back to normal gradually.

DIURETICS

Artificially trying to alter the body's fluid balance is another way in which many people mistakenly believe they can lose fat. This is a misconception because diuretics only reduce your fluid levels. They can cause weight to drop, but as soon as those fluid levels are replaced by taking a drink the weight returns.

Diuretics, either prescribed by a doctor or sold in chemists, can be of help with certain conditions such as premenstrual bloating, but only if used sensibly and correctly. Like laxative abuse, overuse of diuretics depletes the body of essential minerals and vitamins. It can also lead to severe dehydration, as bad as being stranded in the desert with no water. Kidney failure and even heart attacks are not unknown results of severe diuretics abuse.

SLIMMING PILLS

Many compulsive eaters were set on the road to eating problems by taking slimming pills. Such pills may suppress feelings of physical hunger but, as we have noted before, bingeing often has little to do with physical hunger.

Amphetamines, which proved physically addictive and led to so much misery and even death for those hooked on them, are no longer available as a means of losing weight (except from unscrupulous sources). But there are other forms of slimming pills being marketed, and these can be just as psychologically addictive. The fear of putting on weight can make it impossible to give them up.

Slimming pills are no replacement for getting to grips with what is causing your eating problem. Anyone with an eating disorder needs to get back in touch with her true self. Taking pills only makes this more difficult by masking the real picture.

The practice of treating obesity with thyroid tablets has also been abandoned. Taking excess thyroid has a similar effect to going on a crash diet – much of the weight lost is protein tissue. This lack of protein tissue causes your metabolic rate to slow down, so you regain weight more quickly once the treatment stops.

Taking thyroid when there is no natural deficiency causes the thyroid gland to stop working, leading to a dependency on the pills. If the pills are taken in excessive doses this can lead to serious side-effects and heart conditions.

A NORMAL DIET

People with eating disorders rarely have a balanced diet. This can lead to real chemical imbalances, physical illness and emotional instability.

It is easy to slip into the vicious circle of eating snacks such as cakes and sweets because you feel too tired to prepare a proper meal and then continuing to feel tired because your diet is inadequate.

Tiredness is often caused by low blood sugar levels, but it can also be a result of insufficient protein or be a sign of anaemia if you are not getting enough iron. This tiredness could be at the root of the depression, lethargy, headaches and other physical complaints that aggravate an eating disorder. It is amazing how people can perk up tremendously after four days of good sensible eating stabilizes their blood sugar levels.

When Amanda started looking pale and spotty and complaining that she was too tired to go out in the evenings, a friend insisted she go to the doctor. The doctor confirmed that she was anaemic and prescribed a course of iron pills, but he did not question her closely about her eating habits. It would have been much better if he had asked her if she were eating properly: he would have discovered that she lived on a poor diet that provided her body with almost no naturally occurring iron, so it was hardly surprising she was depleted in this mineral (and in various other vitamins and minerals).

CARE FOR YOUR BODY

All this may sound rather complicated and daunting, but don't worry, you don't need to be a biochemist to take good care of yourself.

Think of your body as your best friend, or if you are an animal lover, treat your body as fondly as you would a beloved pet. You probably react with horror to stories of beagles being forced to smoke cigarettes, yet you let yourself take in these same poisons, willingly. You buy fresh fish for your cat but go short on nutritious protein yourself. Once you have learned to like yourself you will appreciate how much your body does for you and you will look after it with more respect.

7 When the Binge Takes Over

Someone who thinks she is a stone overweight decides to diet severely for a couple of weeks and loses quite a bit of weight. Then she reaches a plateau where the weight no longer seems to come off so she eats even less. Hunger builds up and she experiences her first binge, an overwhelming desire to stuff herself with all the sorts of food she has been denying herself. From this point, unless she adopts an appropriate diet that is nourishing and satisfying while allowing her to shed excess fat at a sensible rate, she is going to sink deeper into the diet/binge trap. A couple of months later there will be another binge, a month after that another, a week later another. When she feels premenstrual she'll binge, when she has a row she'll binge, when she is facing a problem she'll binge. An eating disorder will be firmly established.

While the physical body is kept satisfied, physical hunger can easily be distinguished from emotional need. Adopting a strict diet, on the other hand, often marks the beginning of a loss of the ability to recognize true physical hunger. There is little point in assuming that someone whose eating problems have progressed this far will recognize that after not eating for three days she will be hungry. The compulsive eater often does not acknowledge physical hunger, she only recognizes the sudden overwhelming desire to eat and thinks it is due to some weakness in her personality.

Even while this person is being driven to binge by hunger she may say, and believe, she is not 'hungry'. The feeling she is experiencing is something she can only recognize as greed or weakness or perhaps self-hatred. Then comes the guilt, feelings of failure, lowering of self-worth and yet more negative emotion. She was probably already suffering from feelings of low self-esteem when she began to diet, driven by a desire to become suddenly slimmer to make herself feel more attractive. Her lowering of self-worth has only been exaggerated by her failure to stick to the diet of the day.

PHYSICAL BALANCE

It is a myth that eating disorders are all to do with emotional problems. A lot are to do with the physical state of the body, and in some cases just getting this sorted out will be enough to banish the problem completely.

At the age of 14 Sonya thought she was too fat and went on a crash diet. From then on she never ate properly, she was always on some kind of a diet (in between massive bouts of overeating) and never took in sufficient vitamins, protein, fibre and other essential nourishment for her body's needs. At the age of 35 she discovered the Eating Plan described in this book. Within a week she was a different person. Twenty years of not eating properly were swept aside and for the first time her body was being properly nourished. Immediately she lost the urge to binge. Because she felt so much better physically she had the energy and ambition to sort out the emotional problems that were dragging her down. Most of these, she soon discovered, had their roots in her eating problems. For example, she could now accept invitations to go out to dinner or spend weekends visiting friends, because she was not constantly worried about whether she would be overcome by the urge to binge. She gave notice at her well-paid but stressful job because she no longer needed huge amounts of money to support her massive bingeing habit. She went to work in a garden centre where she was able to indulge her love of plants.

Of course Sonya's story is an extreme one – not all compulsive eaters are so badly malnourished, nor can they all respond so quickly. But in general, anyone who has been abusing her body by eating poorly will feel better rapidly when she begins to eat regular, nourishing meals.

HIGHS AND LOWS

The longing to lose weight colours everything when someone is obsessed with dieting. The image of life within a slender body shines before her like a glimpse of heaven, and any path that seems to make progress towards that divine goal gives a tremendous lift to her emotions.

Fasting is used in certain religious practices to give a detachment from the body and heightened spiritual awareness, but these are advanced techniques that can only be followed by those who have studied and prepared themselves on a spiritual level. Dabbling with fasting as a way to feel good is highly dangerous, yet the compulsive eater is so driven by her obsession she is prepared to risk her health and emotional stability for the buzz of weighing less.

'When I eat next to nothing something inside says if I feel this good now, surely I'll feel better if I don't eat anything at all,' says one compulsive eater. This statement is typical of the thinking that lies behind eating compulsions. However, she then adds a significant comment: 'This worries me because it is the start of the binge cycle.' Although hooked on the longing to lose weight, she knows from experience that starvation leads to bingeing. Sooner or later she will break the iron band of fasting and cram herself with food. As long as she craves the buzz of not eating she will be a binger, constantly swinging between extremes and unable to find any happy, peaceful place in between.

THE WAY OUT

The first step towards stopping bingeing is to stop 'starving', whether for you this word means eating nothing at all or merely cutting down so drastically that you are denying yourself adequate nourishment.

This is very hard for many people to accept, but those who are unable to give up their extreme dieting habits will never get their eating under control. When eating has slipped out of control the first priority must be to relearn eating habits that fulfil the body's physical needs.

Those who are overweight will find their figure improves almost immediately when they eat sensibly and are able to break away from destructive calorie-laden binges. This can happen very quickly if bingeing has caused puffiness, particularly around the face and hands.

Rose changed to sensible eating after years of dieting and bingeing. A week later a friend walked straight past her in the street. When she caught her arm her friend looked at her in amazement and said she hadn't recognized her with her new-found sparkling eyes, fresh-looking skin and confident posture.

Those who are not overweight but who have an obsessive longing to be unreasonably thin will learn to appreciate themselves as they are, once they have worked on getting first their eating and then their whole lives back on a straight, even course.

In the long term not just weight loss but the whole quality of life is more satisfactory when eating is under control. Table 13 shows how this works by comparing a week in the eating life of two women, Jane and Claire.

Jane is in a panic because she is going on holiday and has set herself the target of losing 10 pounds before she goes. Her attempts at semi-starvation lead to uncontrolled binges, and by the first day of her holiday she actually weighs two pounds more than she did before she started her 'diet'.

Claire, after years of eating habits similar to Jane's, has realized that getting her eating under control is more important than quick weight loss. She has committed herself to following the eating plan recommended to her and at the end of the week is delighted to find she has also lost weight. All her puffiness has gone as well, making her look slimmer.

Although at first glance Claire seems to be eating more than Jane, and is in fact taking in more calories at each meal, she is not suffering from the urge to binge, so over the week her total calorie intake is in fact much less.

Table 13 COMPARISON OF CLAIRE'S DIET AND JANE'S DIET

CLAIRE			JANE		
Monday		**Calories**	**Monday**		**Calories**
½ pt skimmed milk			5 oz carton of natural low-fat		
(daily allowance)		100	yogurt with ½ oz		
			natural bran		104
Breakfast			5 oz tinned baked beans		
1 satsuma	approx.	30	with tomato sauce		100
1 boiled egg (size one)		95	1 fruit gum		5
¾ oz wholemeal bread		50	3½ oz cucumber		10
			Fresh lemon drink – no sugar		2
Snack			2 oz raw carrot		13
1 crispbread		25	Fresh lemon drink – no sugar		2
1 cheese triangle		40			
1 tomato		10			
Lunch					
3½ oz tinned tuna fish in brine		110			
Large green salad	approx.	20			
½ banana	approx.	50			
5 oz carton natural low-fat					
yogurt		75			
Snack					
1 oz boiled lean ham		60			
1 apple	approx.	50			
Dinner					
Tin game consommé		50			
3 oz grilled liver		150			
Greens	approx.	12			
½ jacket potato without					
butter	approx.	50			
Evening Snack					
¾ oz wholemeal bread		50			
1 oz tinned sardines in					
tomato sauce		52			
		1,079			**236**

CLAIRE

Tuesday	Calories
½ pt skimmed milk (daily allowance)	100

Breakfast
4 oz smoked haddock with butter	145
1 grilled tomato	10
½ grapefruit approx.	15

Snack
2 oz cottage cheese	54
¾ oz wholemeal bread	50

Lunch
2 oz chicken breast, roasted without skin	84
Green salad approx.	20

Snack
½ oz Brie Cheese	44
1 orange approx.	70

Dinner
Slice melon approx.	25
4 oz lean roast lamb	288
3½ oz cabbage, boiled	14
4 oz strawberries	28

Evening Snack
1 crispbread	25
1 oz tinned tuna in brine	27
1 tomato	10
	__1,009__

JANE

Tuesday	Calories
Black cherry yogurt	175
1 oz natural bran	29
5 fruit gums	25
4½ oz raw mushrooms	17
1 fruit gum	5
Fresh lemon drink – no sugar	2
10 oz cabbage, boiled	40
	__293__

CLAIRE

Wednesday	Calories
½ pt skimmed milk (daily allowance)	100

Breakfast

2 oz canned pears	39
1 boiled egg	95
1½ oz wholemeal bread	100

Snack

2 oz cottage cheese	54
1 crispbread	25
1 orange approx.	70

Lunch

2 oz lean boiled ham	120
Large green salad approx.	25

Snack

1 cheese triangle	40
2 tomatoes	20

Dinner

Pheasant consommé	50
2 cod steaks, grilled	160
6 oz cauliflower, boiled	18
4 oz carrots, boiled	20
4 oz blackberries, stewed without sugar	28

Evening Snack

5 oz carton natural low-fat yogurt	75
	1,039

JANE

Wednesday	Calories
Swiss roll, jam and vanilla, 6 oz	600
5 oz carton single cream	300
6 slices bread, butter and jam (large slices and portions) approx.	1,400
Tin of rice pudding, 15½ oz	490
1 can custard	425
20 chocolate triangles	1,000
2 doughnuts	380
2 chocolate bars	595
	5,190

CLAIRE

Thursday		Calories
½ pt skimmed milk (daily allowance)		100

Breakfast

½ grapefruit	approx.	15
1 boiled egg (size one)		95
¾ oz wholemeal bread		50

Snack

1 oz lean boiled ham		60
1 satsuma	approx.	30

Lunch

3 oz tinned crab		120
Large green salad	approx.	30
1 peach	approx.	50

Snack

½ oz Brie cheese		44
2 sticks celery		8

Dinner

Slice melon	approx.	25
4 oz lean roast pork, no fat		212
4 oz broccoli, boiled		20
½ jacket potato without butter	approx.	50
4 oz fresh pineapple		52
3 tablespoons yogurt	approx.	30

Evening Snack

1 oz tinned tuna fish in brine	50
1 crispbread	25
	1,066

JANE

Thursday	Calories
5 oz carton of natural low-fat yogurt with ½ oz natural bran	104
2 crispbreads	50
10 mls Marmite (approx. 2 level teaspoons)	20
1 oz watercress	4
10 fruit gums	50
Fresh lemon drink – no sugar	2
1 fruit gum	5
10 oz cabbage, boiled	40
Fresh lemon drink – no sugar	2
2 fruit gums	10
	287

CLAIRE

Friday	Calories
½ pt skimmed milk (daily allowance)	100

Breakfast

2 oz canned pilchards	70
1½ oz wholemeal bread	100
1 tomato	10

Snack

Triangle cheese	40
1 crispbread	25
1 tomato	10

Lunch

4 oz prawns		120
Large green salad	approx.	25
1 apple	approx.	50

Snack

5 oz carton natural low-fat yogurt	75

Dinner

Liver with onion		190
½ jacket potato without butter	approx.	50
3 oz runner beans, boiled		21
2 oz strawberries and 1 oz grapefruit		20

Evening Snack

1 oz Cheddar cheese	120
1 crispbread	25
	1,051

JANE

Friday	Calories
5 oz carton of natural low-fat yogurt with ½ oz natural bran	104
10 fruit gums	50
Fresh lemon drink – no sugar	2
10 oz cauliflower, boiled	30
16 fl. oz (approx. 4 glasses) sweet white wine	400
4 oz muesli with 1 pt milk	770
2 peanut butter and banana sandwiches approx.	1,040
Large portion fish and chips (bought from local shop) approx.	1,100
2 oz tomato ketchup	60
½ pt lager	120
20 chocolate triangles	1,000
	4,676

CLAIRE

Saturday	Calories
½ pt skimmed milk (daily allowance)	100

Breakfast
1 boiled egg (size one)	95
¾ oz wholemeal bread	50
1 tangerine approx.	30

Snack
1½ oz tinned crab	60
1 tomato	10

Lunch
2 oz roast chicken, breast without the skin	84
Green salad approx.	25
4 oz canned pears	78

Snack
2 oz cottage cheese	54
1 apple approx.	50

Dinner
Cod in parsley sauce	175
½ jacket potato without butter approx.	50
3 oz runner beans, boiled	21
Green salad approx.	25
2 oz strawberries and 1 oz grapefruit	20

Evening Snack (taken in the pub)
2 oz peanuts	336
1 'slimline' shandy	15
	1,278

JANE

Saturday	Calories
5 oz carton of natural low-fat yogurt with ½ oz natural bran	104
10 fruit gums	50
2 crispbreads	50
10 mls Marmite (approx. 2 level teaspoons)	20
1 oz cucumber	3
Fresh lemon drink – no sugar	2
11 oz cauliflower, boiled	33
1 fruit gum	5
	267

CLAIRE

Sunday	Calories
½ pt skimmed milk (daily allowance)	100

Breakfast

1 boiled egg (size one)	95
1½ oz wholemeal bread	100
½ pt skimmed milk	100

Snack

1 apple	approx.	40
1 oz lean boiled ham		60

Lunch

4 oz cottage cheese		108
Large green salad	approx.	30
1 orange	approx.	50

Snack

½ oz Cheddar cheese	60
1 tomato	10

Dinner

4 oz lean roast beef		220
3 oz cauliflower, boiled		9
2 oz carrots, boiled		10
4 oz brussels sprouts, boiled		20
3 tablespoons natural low-fat yogurt	approx.	30

Evening Snack

1 oz tinned sardines in tomato sauce		52
Tomato and cucumber salad	approx.	25
		1,119

Week's total calorie intake 7,641

JANE

Sunday	Calories
5 oz carton of natural low-fat yogurt with ½ oz natural bran	104
2 crispbreads	50
10 mls Marmite (approx. 2 level teaspoons)	20
1 oz cucumber	3
Fresh lemon drink – no sugar	2
1 fruit gum	5
8 oz cabbage, boiled	32
Fresh lemon drink – no sugar	2
3½ oz cucumber	10
	228

Week's total calorie intake 11,177

WHO'S REALLY IN CONTROL?

The sense of being in control that sticking to a crash diet gives is a false high that can never last. Sooner or later the diet will be broken; the resulting plummet from 'high' to 'low' is devastating.

Although restricting food intake has a lot to do with the desire to be in control, many people report that on very low-calorie diets they feel they are not the ones holding the reins.

'The Devil' one woman calls the controller, because all her higher and finer feelings get buried. 'I could do anything when I am on a very low-calorie diet and have become obsessed with the idea of a binge,' she says. 'I could commit a crime and not even know it.' This is borne out by the story of another binger who was driving her car while cramming food into her mouth. She was so distracted by her craving to eat that she knocked someone down on a pedestrian crossing and did not even realize there had been an accident until the police stopped her.

OBSESSION

The mind can become so completely obsessed by the body's cravings that there is no reality and the truth becomes obscured. This makes it very difficult for anyone in the grip of an eating compulsion to seek help. Many women completely baffle their doctors by asking for treatment for physical symptoms without mentioning how their eating habits are causing the problem. Chronic indigestion, painful haemorrhoids and infertility are just three of the adverse effects of abusing the body through bingeing, starvation and purging. If a chronic binger goes to the doctor complaining of stomach pains and does not tell him or her that she binges, the doctor cannot begin to help her effectively. This is not helped by the unfortunate fact that many doctors are unaware how widespread serious eating disorders are, and receive no training in how to recognize or deal with patients who are compulsive eaters.

A patient cannot be helped in the long term if she complains of depression but does not mention a food obsession that is completely dominating her mind. It is unlikely her doctor will ask her directly about her eating habits, and she is just as unlikely to volunteer information.

The power of an eating obsession can be at the root of almost any physical or emotional problem. Many chronic sufferers do not actually link medical conditions with their eating abuse. It does not occur to them that swallowing over a hundred laxatives a day could cause internal bleeding, or that days of starvation could lead to insomnia. Such is the power of their obsession that they have become completely out of touch with the realities of their body and their lives.

Laura went to her doctor because of pains in her stomach. She told the doctor she was being sick several times a day and vomiting up blood. Her doctor was naturally very concerned and sent her off for extensive tests to discover why she was being sick. Laura did not tell him – it did not occur to her to tell him – that she was making herself sick because she suffered badly from bulimia nervosa, so it was hardly surprising that the doctors were baffled and could find no successful way to treat her.

The inability to link physical symptoms with an eating disorder is not necessarily just due to shame or dishonesty. It is a product of the muddled thinking that takes over the compulsive eater's mind. She has become so used to living with her way of life she no longer connects it with the cause of physical symptoms or views it as a deliberate act of personal sabotage.

WHAT IS A BINGE?

Mindless eating, unplanned eating – these are sure signs that eating is out of control. The distress bingeing brings often bears little relation to the amount eaten – an indication of the deep emotional problems finding expression through overeating.

Maria sat in her kitchen at 2 a.m. crying her heart out and desperately wanting to die. She had just eaten a small tin of baked beans. To her this was an admission of total failure.

Until then the day had gone well. She had been to visit friends for dinner and drove home easily ignoring the temptations of late-night take-away shops. But once back alone in the kitchen the urge to eat something was overpowering. It was almost as if she was standing back watching herself opening the tin of beans, heating them up and stuffing them urgently into her mouth.

Maria's distress, almost to the point of suicide, was inappropriate to the consumption of a few baked beans. If she were not so distraught she would have realized that:

1. her blood sugar levels would be low at 2 a.m., leading to a physical need for food,
2. people often have a snack when coming home in the early hours – those without an eating problem would think it a normal and desirable habit, and
3. protein-packed beans were a sensible thing to eat at that time and in those circumstances; they were just what her body needed.

BINGE FOODS

Many people say that when they binge it tends to be on the sort of foods they don't normally eat. If they know they have an eating problem and want to treat their body with respect they work hard at avoiding foods that are not healthy or nutritious. Refined foods like white bread, cakes and sweets full of sugar are generally the sort of things to be avoided. In calm, sensible times everyone knows this. However, when control slips away and the urge to binge becomes overwhelming, the compulsive eater is often drawn to these very things. They are often the easiest things to buy and eat urgently, and they represent the very opposite of everything that person is striving to achieve. These foods are not so much a treat as a punishment – a binge is not a happy, fun event. Starchy, sweet foods fill up the emptiness, high-calorie foods make the eater put on weight in spite of her less self-destructive side that wants only to be healthy.

OVERWHELMING DESIRE

When bingeing becomes a really serious problem it begins to overwhelm daily life completely. The urge to binge wipes out everything, there is no other reality.

Louise reached the stage where her eating habits had become so out of control she risked losing her job. She had become unreliable and her concentration wandered because when the urge to binge crept up on her she lost touch with reality.

Louise had suffered from compulsive eating problems most of her life, but when times were good she felt more or less in control. A catalogue of disasters and bereavements plunged her into an emotional low that allowed her eating disorder to rear up and swamp her until she became suicidal with the strain of the powerful emotions battling inside her.

The first indications that a major binge was looming would be constant thoughts about the binge. She would dream about it at night and wake up knowing there was no escape. She would find herself planning her binge with great precision and setting out on a mammoth shopping expedition.

The first stop would be a local shop to get something to eat *while* she was buying everything she needed for her binge. Then she would go from shop to shop buying a few items here, a few more there – so nobody would guess what she was planning. She felt compelled to make up unnecessary stories to shopkeepers or others in the checkout queues about buying biscuits because some imaginary children were coming to visit, or that the chocolate was a present for a friend.

Sometimes she would make a long journey to the other side of town to buy some special cake she craved. Reason and common sense were completely set aside; she had no awareness of how much money she was spending or even if she had the money to spend. She shopped in a jumbled daze with only the concept of what she had to buy clear in her mind. If she happened to meet an acquaintance in the street she could not bear to stop and talk and was frequently quite rude to people in her urgency to return home.

When at last she was home, with the doors locked to prevent even the slightest risk of anyone discovering her, she would eat, cramming food into her mouth with such urgency that she once bit her finger almost through to the bone.

Six loaves of white bread, a pound of butter, two pots of jam, five bars of chocolate, eight doughnuts, a pint of cream . . . the food kept being crammed in until it seemed impossible a human stomach could hold much more. The solid food was all washed down with plenty of fluid. Louise knew that sooner or later she would have to vomit it all up, and that would be impossible if it were too solid a mass.

As the binge continued, Louise would get breathless and the pain in her stomach would increase until she felt barely able to walk. Still she could not stop until everything had been consumed. Then would come the vomiting, as all that food was regurgitated. Finally Louise would collapse into bed, racked with pain and too exhausted to feel the full force of her distress. She lay there totally wrecked and vowing she would never, never binge again. But gradually she would recover and the terrible urge to binge would creep up on her again.

Louise would react to her binge by a strong urge to clean away every scrap of evidence. All the crumbs and wrappers were packed away in the dustbin, the toilet into which she had vomited was cleaned, disinfected and even scrubbed minutely with an old toothbrush, then she would bath herself, perhaps twice over, using disinfectant in the water to try and wash away the dirty feeling.

Although many serious bingers do react with this mania for total cleanliness, others do the opposite. Stephanie had a special old dress she called her 'binge dress' which she would put on before starting to stuff herself with food. She ate in a disgusting way, cramming food in her mouth and not caring what got spilt over her and the furniture, scattering packets and wrappings all around the room. She would binge at weekends, a release from the strain of the working week, hiding herself away from Friday night until Monday morning, not washing, cleaning her teeth or tidying the house.

Such extreme behaviour reflects serious emotional problems. Self-control has completely broken down. The rules of conventional social behaviour are cast aside and the person is isolated and cast out of the everyday world. Bingeing is her only reality.

Most bingers, even those who have not got a serious problem, know their table manners degenerate during a binge. Carol consulted an eminent doctor about her eating problem and he told her the answer was simple: when she had eaten enough she merely had to put down her knife and fork. She left his expensive session angry and disappointed, because despite the inflated fee this man obviously had absolutely no idea what compulsive eating was all about. She did not dare tell him that when she binged she stuffed food straight from the packets into her mouth - there were no knife and fork to put down, and no plate to put them on!

The urgency of the need to eat does not allow for laying the table, using a knife and fork, cooking and preparing meals. Binge food is usually easy to buy and eat: ready-cooked items such as cakes and pies, things like bread, and of course chocolate, which only needs to be torn out of its paper wrapping.

Binge food is usually gulped down with a feeling of panic and immediacy, the binger eating fast not only to get the food down quickly but often because of a fear of being discovered.

Afterwards, disgust with her eating habits is added to the list of the negative feelings such as guilt and low self-esteem that the binger feels about not being able to control her eating.

8 The Bulimic

Compulsive eaters like Louise (in Chapter 7) are also suffering from the condition called *bulimia nervosa*. The bulimic will prevent some of the food she eats from working through her digestive system in a normal way. Usually this is done with the conscious thought that she does not want to put on weight. Many bulimics were once anorexic and are not used to the feeling of food in their stomachs. They don't like the discomfort they experience if they eat more than they are used to eating.

The most widely known way in which the bulimic prevents full digestion is by making herself sick after eating. She discovers that it is very difficult to make herself vomit up tiny amounts of food, so she has another excuse to binge on huge amounts, also drinking plenty of fluids to make it easier to bring up afterwards.

There are other habits that prevent the body absorbing food; these also come under the general title of bulimia. Taking large numbers of laxatives is one. The idea behind this is to speed food through the system thus preventing it being properly digested. Although a proportion does go straight through, much of the food in this case is digested. The whole issue is quite complex but it is certainly advisable not to abuse laxatives with a view to losing weight. At the Maisner Centre there are clients weighing over 15 stone who abuse laxatives, which proves it does not work effectively. Then there are diuretics, which reduce body fluid thus causing a temporary weight loss. Even taking exercise is classed as bulimic behaviour when it becomes compulsive and a person's main aim is to prevent weight-gain rather than to become fit.

Bulimia can develop out of another eating problem. As a compulsive eater's fast/binge pattern becomes more and more firmly established it becomes necessary for her to go to ever further extremes if she is to remain 'in control' of her weight. Slimming clubs and crash diets can inadvertently lead people down the road to bulimia. If a club member has not stuck to her diet and knows she will have to face the 'disgrace' of not having lost weight, she may resort to making herself sick to achieve a drastic (if temporary) weight loss. Many bulimics report coming across the idea of making themselves sick by accident. They had eaten or drunk too much and vomited naturally, then, realizing what a relief this brought, began to think about doing it deliberately. They use it to get rid of the after-effects of bingeing ~ both the physical feeling of fullness and the guilt at having submitted to a craving ~ and to prevent putting on weight.

Sharon became a bulimic on New Year's Eve. It was one of those evenings that start badly and grow steadily worse. She and her boyfriend argued early in the evening about going to a party. He wanted to go, she was feeling fat and miserable after overeating at Christmas. When she tried on her favourite party dress and found it was too tight she threw a tantrum. Eventually they did go to the party and both had too much to drink. Shortly before midnight Sharon's boyfriend was very sick and fell asleep in a corner of the room. Furiously angry, Sharon decided that she would be sick as well just to show him.

The next day she felt dreadful and vowed she would never do anything like that again, but a couple of days later after a large meal she found herself thinking about how easy it had been to make herself sick and empty out her uncomfortable stomach. Within three months she was completely addicted to the habit. When things were going really wrong she would be sick three or four times a day. At first she found she was losing weight with constant vomiting and this gave her such a buzz it encouraged her to do it more often. But then she noticed she was eating larger amounts as her binges became more frantic and the weight was no longer coming off steadily. She could vary by almost a stone in weight within a few days as she swung between huge binges and desperate vomiting. Her mother became alarmed because she looked so pale and ill; her boyfriend walked out on her because he could not understand or cope with her moods.

Sharon went through a pattern that is typical of the beginning of bulimia. She told herself she would just do it once, or only occasionally in dire circumstances. She did not realize how easily bulimia can become a compulsive habit. Many bulimics report similar experiences.

Not all compulsive eaters are bulimics, of course. For many their uncontrolled eating stops short of vomiting and purging. Nor are all bulimics compulsive eaters, as there are some people who eat normal regular meals but then make themselves sick afterwards out of habit. Many bulimics are underweight or only about half a stone over their ideal weight - as they are often dehydrated, however, being underweight may just be a result of their low levels of body fluids. Many are very overweight, proving this is not a successful way to get slim. It is certainly a very unhealthy and expensive habit, and if not caught and dealt with early it can do lasting damage to the body.

Many bulimics develop the condition out of anorexia, and although many anorexics binge and make themselves sick and many bulimics go through times when they starve themselves, there are marked differences between the two conditions.

As can be seen in Table 15, the anorexic tends to refuse to recognize that she has a problem. Because of this she is not likely to seek out help to enable her to change her life away from her anorexia. She feels rigidly in control and does not want anyone to take that control away from her. She needs to be treated by those who specialize in anorexia nervosa.

WHO IS BULIMIC?

Statistics covering known cases show that the majority of bulimics start the habit between the ages of 16 and 45, but it can hit at any age. Nearly half of those who suffer from anorexia are likely to develop bulimia. The bulimic can be an introverted person who is dependent on others, but equally she may be an extrovert, socially capable person. This is what can make the bulimic so difficult to spot, particularly as she is often of average weight and appears cheerful and in control. She is not the sort of person one would immediately recognize as having a problem, unlike the anorexic who may stand out in a crowd due to her terrible thinness.

Surveys of university students have shown that anything from one in 25 to one in eight female students are bulimic or have the criteria for it. Such studies cannot be relied on as totally accurate because of the extremely secretive nature of bulimia. It can be assumed that any survey is likely to miss a large percentage of sufferers, so it is hardly surprising that the average person says 'I

Table 14 COMPARISON CHART OF ANOREXIC, BULIMIC AND COMPULSIVE EATER

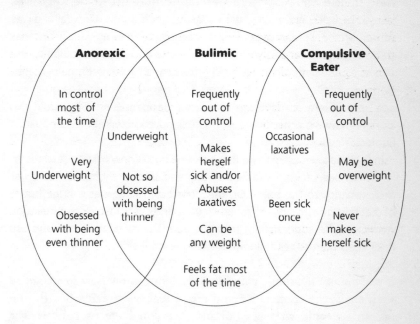

The **Anorexic** is generally:

Mostly in control

Wants to be thinner
and becomes obsessed with
being very thin

Refuses to accept
anything is wrong

Won't seek help

The **Bulimic** is generally:

Mostly out of control

Feels self-disgust and
anger at her loss of control

Knows something is wrong

May seek help

don't know any bulimics.' If you are a bulimic yourself you are probably able to spot the tell-tale signs in others.

Lynn thought she was an expert at hiding the signs of her bulimia. She was a student who outwardly appeared cheerful and capable, was always seen to be working hard and generally got good marks. One day she was sitting in the library apparently absorbed in reading when another student came up and sat next to her. 'I'm so sorry you are bulimic,' she said in a soft, sympathetic voice. 'I am too and I have been helped a lot by my counsellor. Here is her address and phone number.' The other girl got up and left, leaving Lynn absolutely flabbergasted. She could not imagine how the other girl could possibly have known about her bulimic habit.

In fact the signs were there for someone who knew how to read them. Lynn had been taking laxatives all day and frequently had to leave her desk for trips to the toilet. On the floor beside her was a huge bottle of diet cola from which she took frequent drinks – a favourite of bulimics, who crave the additional lift they get from the caffeine in cola and use it to keep themselves full without calorie intake.

If you are not a bulimic yourself and do not know how to recognize such signs, the chances are you are probably acquainted with one or more people who are bulimic. Yet you have probably never guessed nor even considered that they might have this problem.

Gina was the popular landlady of a large pub. Always bright and on the go, slim and smartly dressed, many people envied her as the woman who really seemed to have it all. When friends came to visit they received lavish hospitality and were invited to sit down and enjoy a meal in the pub's thriving restaurant. Nobody ever thought it odd that Gina never sat down to eat with them – she was always so busy – nor that she never cooked for them in her private apartment. It was only when Tina was introduced to her that her secret came near to being discovered. Tina had suffered from bulimia for several years but had managed to get over it. She immediately recognized that there was something not quite right about Gina's behaviour. She noticed how Gina was never seen eating in front of anyone, how she spoke in tones of thinly disguised disgust about her customers who ate large meals and enjoyed sugary, fattening puddings. A little conversation soon unearthed a few facts about Gina's life: a broken home, two failed marriages, a miscarriage. The pub staff confirmed that there were times when Gina demanded to be left alone in her apartment and not to be disturbed whatever the problem. They understood she needed time off, but Tina saw this as more evidence of Gina's battle with eating.

Tina's dilemma was how to tackle Gina and persuade her to get help. She decided to sit down and tell her the story of her own fight with bulimia, hoping this would encourage Gina to confide in someone who understood. Gina's response was quite the opposite. She grew very guarded and cut the conversation short, saying she had just remembered something important that had to be done. From that day on Gina avoided her, but Tina was not surprised to learn a couple of years later that Gina had collapsed with a mysterious illness, sold the pub and was living alone in a cottage in the depths of the country.

This story shows how easily bulimia can be hidden. The average bulimic is an intelligent person well able to cover her tracks and appear to be living a successful life. Under this surface, however, there is a dark and miserable lie going on. Many bulimics do not know how to handle the problems in their lives in an appropriate manner or how to cope with what they see as their own personal failures. Some punish themselves with bingeing and vomiting, others use it to comfort themselves, others to block out reality. They tell themselves that as long as they remain slim and seemingly capable they are handling their lives. Every bulimic, however, is on borrowed time. The ideal image she projects becomes more and more of a sham as the shady world of bulimia takes over more and more of her life.

Tracey left home at the age of 16 and went to live in a bed-sitter. She already knew that she had a problem about food. She would eat too much and indulge in large binges in between attempts to diet. She also realized she was gradually putting on weight and started to panic even though she was nowhere near being seriously overweight.

Not knowing where to turn she consulted her doctor, who could see at a glance that she was not obese. Unable to offer much practical advice he told her her weight was fine and that as long as she continued to eat healthy foods there was no problem. His parting piece of advice was that she go and buy a pound of carrots.

So Tracey got on with her life and, being intelligent and hard working, by the age of 19 she had a good job. At 19 she also realized that, bit by bit, she had become bulimic. Whenever she felt under stress she noticed her concentration wandering and the urge to binge taking over. Relationships started to fall apart when people came second to eating in her life.

She tried the doctor again, and this time he referred her to a psychiatrist. A week of intensive therapy left her feeling even more isolated. Other patients were suffering from alcoholism or depression – next to them her problem was difficult to recognize.

'Other people get smashed when they have problems,' she said. 'I don't drink, bingeing is my only safety valve.'

And so Tracey continues to get by in a weird split world. Smartly dressed she works efficiently all day, others see her as a bubbly person, in control of her life. But away from work and inside her head she feels scatty and muddled. At home she dresses scruffily and her life revolves around bingeing. It has come to be the only way of life she knows.

Tracey's is a classic case of bulimia. She lives alone, both to give herself the privacy to indulge in her bingeing and because she finds it difficult to maintain relationships.

AN ENDLESS CIRCLE

As we have mentioned about other eating disorders, the emotional problems that lead to bulimia are only one side of the story. It is possible to become bulimic through physical disturbances of body chemistry, without any great load of emotional trauma on top. In such cases the emotional problems come later and are mainly caused by struggling to handle life as a bulimic.

The physical side of the binge/diet syndrome is illustrated well by Barbara French in her book *Coping With Bulimia*, which describes it as an endless circle – once entered there is no obvious way out.

The initial desire to be slim, perhaps as a result of being teased for being fat as a child or so as to look like a pop or screen idol, initiates the first diet. Then the physical circle takes over and the sufferer goes on and on, bingeing and dieting and becoming increasingly more miserable.

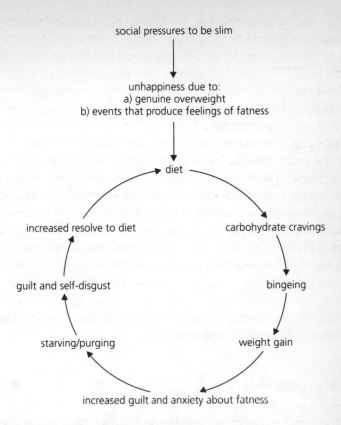

social pressures to be slim

unhappiness due to:
a) genuine overweight
b) events that produce feelings of fatness

diet

increased resolve to diet

carbohydrate cravings

guilt and self-disgust

bingeing

starving/purging

weight gain

increased guilt and anxiety about fatness

Figure 7

LOVING SUPPORT

It takes a special kind of partner to give a bulimic the real support she needs, and even the most loving mate can unknowingly make things worse or have his best intentions misinterpreted. Thinking becomes more muddled as the bulimic state worsens, it becomes more and more difficult to recognize people and situations as they really are. Everything becomes interpreted in relationship to its relevance to eating.

There is also another kind of bulimic who, instead of hiding her behaviour in the classic way, seems to flaunt her ability to make herself sick whenever she feels life is not treating her well. Some women discover they can wield tremendous power, particularly over their close family, by this kind of behaviour. Others use it as a weapon to punish those who have hurt them, or who they believe are hurting them.

Instead of developing into mature adults these bulimics get stuck in the mindset of spoiled children. They may threaten their partners with 'If you go out tonight I shall sit at home and eat and eat until I'm sick, and then you'll be sorry.'

Sarah was a bulimic married to an actor. Although her husband was devoted and faithful to her, Sarah tormented herself with the thought of him working and socializing with actresses – slim actresses. She grew obsessed with the idea of becoming thinner than the thinnest of them.

She dieted, binged, made herself sick and destroyed her peace of mind in her obsessive pursuit of slimness. As eating took over most of her waking thoughts her relationship with her husband deteriorated, until one day he did leave her, not for a slender actress but for someone who could give him the love and attention that Sarah could no longer offer.

Situations like this put great strain on families. Support for the bulimic and counselling for those close to her are essential.

WHY BULIMIA?

Some people find that making themselves sick after eating is a way to deal with stress; the physical relief of emptying their stomach seems to be connected to an emotional release from stressful situations or thought patterns.

If you make yourself sick deliberately, consider whether any of the following seems to apply:

1. You feel a sense of relief from tension.
2. You feel calmer, better able to face the world.
3. You feel better able to cope with life or a particular situation.
4. You feel a release from anger and aggression.
5. You feel 'cleaner', both physically and emotionally.
6. You get a buzz of excitement, a relief from boredom and loneliness.
7. You feel you are escaping from the reality of things you find it difficult to face up to.
8. You use it as a diversion from something you do not want to do.

9. You get special attention when you are sick.
10. You feel you are getting your own back on someone or on life in general.
11. You feel you are punishing yourself for all the things you do not like about yourself.
12. You are acting out of habit.
13. You are filling a gap that is not being met by a creative activity.

What To Do

The only way to overcome bulimia is to get to grips with the reason you are making yourself sick. If your eating is in control then usually you will no longer have the need to vomit. The obvious answer to the question 'Why do you make yourself ill?' is the answer, 'To avoid putting on weight.' This is what most bulimics will say when asked.

But there are other ways of not putting on weight, in particular by not bingeing in the first place. It's not easy, of course – bulimia very quickly becomes a habit which is difficult to break. Just as if you give up smoking you will suffer strong physical cravings for nicotine, withdrawal symptoms and emotional upheaval, breaking the bulimia cycle can put you through similar tortures and will require similar strength. Handling the physical urge to empty your stomach and the emotional desire to satisfy one or more of your feelings of tension, anger and other negative emotion will demand real motivation.

There is no easy answer, but once you have identified some of the reasons that are causing you to make yourself sick, consider some of the following:

1. If you are under stress you need to understand what is causing that stress and take immediate action to put things right rather than disguising the root problem with bulimia (see Chapter 14 on coping with stress).
2. There are ways to calm yourself down which will actually improve your health rather than undermine it. Relaxation techniques, yoga, non-competitive sport, fresh air – all these act through the physical body to calm the mind. Once you have achieved peace of mind you will be able to face the world more easily.

3. Actually doing something about a situation you find difficult is usually much easier than worrying about it and avoiding taking action. Fear is often at the root of feeling unable to cope (See Chapter 12 on dealing with fear).

4. Anger, resentment and aggression build up in similar ways to stress, and similar methods of dealing with it are recommended. There is nothing wrong in showing anger in an appropriate manner if you feel it is justified; it can often clear the air in a difficult situation and clear the way for rebuilding a better relationship. Bottled-up anger will only cause damage to yourself or burst out in unreasonable aggression (See Chapter 11 for further guidelines about facing up to and dealing with anger).

5. If you feel the need to cleanse yourself it is because you have a sense of being 'dirty' or of there being something about yourself or your life you do not like. This needs to be faced and come to terms with. It may well be a deep-seated problem that needs professional help and counselling to overcome. Do not feel ashamed of seeking specialized professional help.

6. If the only thing able to give you a thrill in life is being sick, you need to develop more in your life. There is a whole exciting world out there for you to enter and enjoy, but only you can discover it. If you are lonely you can learn social skills to overcome your shyness; getting your eating under control will leave you free to commit yourself to a social life (see chapters 14 and 16 for more detailed advice).

7. If severe bulimia becomes the only reality in life, everything else retreats to a distance at which it becomes manageable. If you have lost touch with real life you are going to have to make some drastic changes to get back on course. You must accept that you are the one who is going to have to do a lot of hard work to achieve this. If there is some particular situation you are escaping from, such as a bad relationship or grief over a bereavement or the memory of a trauma, you will never find peace of mind in any form of escapism such as bulimia. You need professional help and counselling to come to terms with life.

8. Eating is much easier than doing something you don't fancy, whether it is finishing up the leftovers instead of doing the washing up or staying at home to binge instead of going to the

office Christmas party. There are certain chores that have to be done sooner or later – if you never wash up the dirty dishes will eventually take over the kitchen. The best way to tackle these things is to get stuck in and get them over with as quickly as possible, then go and do something pleasant (not bingeing). When it comes to the things that don't really have to be done, but that you feel obliged to do, why binge and feel guilty? Make a rational decision not to put yourself through an unnecessary ordeal: you will not get the sack for missing the office party if you dread the idea of it. Say politely but firmly that you will not be attending then go out and do something you really want to do instead – without feeling guilty.

9. Attention-seeking through bad behaviour is what small children do. Why have you found it so difficult to grow up and face the responsibilities of being an adult? You are responsible for yourself and your actions. You must learn to accept this. You need not always be in the limelight to feel that people care for you. You may need help to achieve the self-confidence you need so that you no longer feel the urge to bribe people for their love and attention in this way. If you begin to care about yourself and other people you can become the sort of person that others naturally seek out as a friend and companion.

10. Although you can make other people feel bad by making yourself sick, in the end you only hurt yourself both physically and emotionally. Trying to impose a burden of guilt on another person may backfire on you, it certainly will not build a strong relationship based on love and trust. If you feel life has dealt you a rough hand, try to learn to think of it as a challenge to be overcome; kicking back at life is a fruitless occupation.

11. What have you done to deserve punishing yourself in such a way? If you don't like how you look, how you behave or the kind of life you lead, go out and take some positive action to improve yourself. Never allow yourself to get off the hook by making excuses, if you really want to make changes you *can* do it.

12. If bulimia has become a habit that is damaging your health, it has to be broken before you become seriously ill. If you can see nothing wrong in being deliberately sick after eating, if you do not think you have a problem – then perhaps you have the biggest problem of all.

13. Everyone needs a form of self-expression. Those with particular

creative talents will become particularly frustrated if they deny themselves any outlet. Bingeing may be the only way in which it seems possible to express who you are and how you feel. Next time you get the urge to binge, try getting a large sheet of paper and drawing out how you are feeling, or put on some music and dance out your emotions. If you have had training in a particular form of artistic expression you should find it possible to rediscover repressed talents. If not, now is the time to join a class, group or workshop that will help you get in touch with your creative self.

9 Seeing the Signs and Offering Support

It can be the most unexpected people who turn out to be bingers or bulimics: the child who was always quiet and well behaved, the teenager who never rebelled. They may have been holding in their emotions for years until they discovered bingeing as the way to express themselves.

It can be very difficult for parents to understand why their children should do this to themselves, or to accept that they may be contributing to the problem. Communication, an open mind and the will to help are essential for anyone involved with a compulsive eater.

Because of the secrecy that usually accompanies bingeing, it is possible for a family to be completely unaware that anything is wrong even though they live with someone with an eating disorder. It may have started in a small way and there could have been times of remission when eating was normal. But as life goes on and stress mounts the problem may grow steadily worse and may exist for years.

WHO HAS A PROBLEM?

There are no hard-and-fast guidelines as to why one particular person should develop an eating disorder, but at the Maisner Centre for Eating Disorders – where people with a wide range of problems focused around food, eating and weight are talked with daily – a cocktail of physical and emotional factors most often emerges: low self-esteem, inability to be assertive, suppressed anger, resentment, lack of fulfilment, sensitivity to various foods and low blood sugar. There is often a connection between depression and eating disorders. Almost everybody, with or without an eating problem, notices a temporary change in their eating patterns when under stress or particularly happy or unhappy. Long-term depression can be associated with a long-term alteration of eating habits. While some depressed people turn to drink or drugs to help them cope with life, others become binge eaters, or binge as well as drink. The reverse is also true: some people lose their appetite because they are depressed or stressed, but the rapid weight loss which results can ultimately lead to bingeing again.

WHERE DOES IT START?

Many people with eating problems can trace a family history of bingeing, alcoholism or depression. Whether this is passed on genetically or through body chemistry, or whether using food and alcohol to 'deal' with life problems is learned behaviour, is not fully understood.

The basic ground for an eating disorder is often laid down in childhood and the teenage years, even though it may not manifest until later in life. Well-meaning parents who want what they consider the best for their children can cause terrible damage by using phrases like 'nice and slim' (subconsciously implying that overweight people are not nice) or by warning their children that people will not like them if they are fat or that nobody will marry them if they are not slim.

Other parents shout or are rude to their children constantly, both at home and in public, saying things like 'shut your mouth' which lower a child's self-esteem and lay the groundwork for further problems later in life.

Chubby children are often teased at school and this can cause life-long emotional problems around food even if that child grows into a slim adult.

Talented children who are not allowed sufficient self-expression, such as the musical child who is told to 'stop that noise' when she plays the piano or the academic child who is pressurized to leave school and go out to work as soon as possible, can develop emotional problems due to frustrated ambitions.

Sweets are often used as weapons with children, withheld as a punishment or given as a reward, or as consolation for a cut knee where a kiss or cuddle would be more appropriate. In this way sweet foods become associated with consoling yourself when things go wrong; denying yourself them becomes a form of punishment.

MOTIVATION

Getting back to a normal life depends on many factors, not least the motivation of the sufferer, possibly coupled with the support of close family and friends. If the problem is not too serious, bingeing is not frequent and the person has a naturally strong constitution, sometimes something like a miracle seems to occur.

Stuart was offered a job in the United States and wanted to look slim when he arrived. He started a five-day fast which someone told him would work wonders. But on the third day he binged, so he had to start the five days all over again; again half-way through he binged. After two months he was in despair and weighed more than before he started the whole process. At that point he discovered the Maisner Eating Plan – within 24 hours of eating normally he was back to his old self. He felt his eating was under control again and he was happy and confident about leaving for the US, resolving never to try fasting or crash dieting again.

For most people, however, it is more difficult to get back in control, and significant changes have to be made to produce the required, far-reaching results. Yet it is not necessarily those with a deep-rooted habit who take the longest to change their attitudes to food and life. If the road back to controlled eating is approached with enough conviction someone with a long-standing problem will see positive results much more quickly than someone with a relatively minor problem who is not truly committed to getting better.

Step by step, thought patterns must be challenged, motives questioned, habits broken. Eating may improve for a while, degenerate under a stressful period, then improve again. Nobody who has been bingeing badly for years should expect to kick the habit in five minutes – although this has been known.

Anne had lived with her eating problems for years and dragged herself miserably through each day. She thought her marriage was unhappy because she always felt so moody and could not get on with her husband. She had few friends because bingeing came before socializing. She became fatter and fatter until one day she suffered a heart attack and the doctor told her if she did not lose weight she would die. This spurred her into getting professional help with her eating. She discovered it was a lot simpler than she had imagined. She found that if she ate a sensible breakfast each morning she was able to resist the temptation to buy a bag of cream buns on her way to work, and by such practical means she learned how to change her eating habits completely. As she lost weight and was no longer obsessed by her eating, other unexpected benefits began to emerge. She felt a much happier person as her mood swings lessened she appreciated her husband more, and he was happy to see her so confident and well. Their relationship improved greatly.

PHYSICAL STATES

It is not easy to recognize the person with a compulsive eating problem. Unlike the alcoholic who may show obvious signs of being drunk, the food addict can be much more secretive. The person who appears to eat very little may in fact be the one who is bingeing in secret.

Depression, anxiety and irrational behaviour can all be signs of an eating disorder, but these are common to so many other states unrelated to eating that such symptoms alone are no sure guide.

Physical effects of bingeing, which could also be attributed to other causes, include:

- abdominal distention and pain
- swelling of the hands, legs, feet
- facial puffiness
- constipation or diarrhoea
- tiredness
- nausea
- breathlessness
- dizziness
- sweating
- irregular heartbeat
- mental confusion
- irrational behaviour
- panic attacks
- depression
- desire for carbohydrates
- low blood sugar

Long-term bingeing and purging play havoc with the body. Even before serious side-effects take hold, low blood sugar levels can cause feelings of panic and depression.

Vomiting places a huge burden on the body. It can cause strain and even tearing of the oesophagus, leading to bleeding. The eyes can also suffer: a burst blood vessel in the eye is not unusual after heavy vomiting.

Severe bouts of bingeing and vomiting can also affect a woman's menstrual cycle. Being very underweight can cause periods to stop completely, but abuse of the digestive and intestinal organs can also lead to missed periods and difficulty in conceiving. Other serious effects of vomiting are:

- irregular heartbeat
- irrational behaviour
- mental confusion
- anxiety
- panic attacks
- depression
- muscular weakness
- poor circulation
- tingling in the fingers and toes
- extremely cold hands
- dehydration
- low blood-pressure
- kidney damage
- swollen salivary glands
- damage to the throat and oesophagus
- ulcers
- hair loss
- dry skin
- dental problems

Teeth give away a lot of secrets. An astute dentist might learn to recognize bulimic patients by the increase in erosion caused by acidic vomit in the mouth.

MENTAL STATES

As can be seen by the above lists, the physical dangers and consequences of binge eating and bulimia are augmented by the emotional stress these conditions impose. A person's moods can swing dramatically or she may experience a general state of depression. When the urge to binge is strong nothing can take precedence. If anyone gets in the way he may be met with anything from vague inattentiveness to outright aggression. The binge eater knows how impossible it is to handle other people when she is in the grip of this overpowering compulsion, so she tends to isolate herself, sometimes by deliberately sabotaging relationships.

The desperate binger is as little in control of her behaviour as is the chronic alcoholic. If she has not got the money to buy the binge food she needs she will steal it. A normally law-abiding person will resort to shoplifting because all moral codes are blurred by her overwhelming need for food. Then she may have to lie and cheat to cover her tracks, bringing on a further load of guilt and increased isolation.

Stealing food, or stealing money to buy food, is something that nearly all compulsive eaters do at some point. But many go further than that: they can steal from shops even when they have plenty of money with them to pay for the goods, or they can steal other items, just because they are feeling out of control.

Susan admitted to having amassed a huge collection of soaps, perfumes, shampoos and other toiletries – much more than she was ever likely to use. She felt compelled to have these things to pamper and comfort herself with because she was so overwhelmed by her compulsive behaviour towards eating and weight.

DANGER SIGNS

If you think a friend or member of the family is a compulsive eater, look out for eating habits that do not seem normal to you. For example, if your daughter always makes an excuse not to join in family meals, quietly check out whether she really is having a large lunch at school each day or eating at a friend's house every evening as she tells you. Some married couples have never eaten a meal together in 20 years, the husband never realizing there was anything strange in this. If your wife always says she has eaten earlier with the children or that she is on a diet and eats only a tiny portion or nothing at all, be alert to these warning signs of an eating problem.

The biggest clue to look out for is usually extreme mood swings. Spouses frequently feel in despair because they cannot understand their partner's behaviour. It never occurs to them that the mood that greets them at home depends entirely on whether she has had a 'good-eating' or a 'bad-eating' day. She may be in a wonderful mood when he leaves for work in the morning, but when he gets home she is in tears and shuts herself in the bedroom refusing to speak to him, or they may have a blazing row in the morning and that evening she is on top of the world. He just doesn't know what is going on and finds life very stressful.

Someone who frequently makes an excuse to go to the bathroom shortly after a meal, particularly if once there she puts the radio on or runs water, may be making herself sick after eating: don't be taken in by stories about going for a bath, or gastroenteritis going round the office.

Another big give-away is fluctuations in weight. Someone who is very thin and a few weeks later seems to have put on a lot of weight, only to lose it again suddenly, could well be bingeing and may also be making herself sick a lot. Clever dressing may hide this, so it is important to be observant if you suspect a compulsive eating problem. Large weight fluctuations are not normal in a healthy person, so if they are not due to food abuse it is important to consult a doctor about a possible underlying medical condition.

STRANGE BEHAVIOUR

The compulsive eater is in a state of chaos even though she may appear calm on the outside. This may manifest as irrational behaviour such as mood swings or in unusual actions such as suddenly deciding to go out shopping or disappearing for several hours with no explanation. Her finances are also likely to be strained. A working person can fall into debt and not be able to explain where the money has gone – it has been spent on food and, possibly, laxatives. A housewife with no income of her own may spend a whole week's housekeeping on one binge and then have to weave an intricate web of deceit to try and explain away the loss. Frequent stories of lost money, stolen purses or mistakes at the bank may be a sign of trying to cover up for spending money on binge food.

Jenny began to make real progress in getting her eating under control and started having regular sessions with a counsellor. After a while her husband Richard went along with her and during the session it came out that Jenny had been spending £5,000 a year on binge food, over and above their agreed grocery budget. Richard said he had wondered why they were always short of money even though they both worked. He knew Jenny had an eating problem but he had never made the connection that she had been spending so much on bingeing.

In a family home or shared house food can mysteriously disappear or food wrappings turn up hidden in drawers and cupboards: these are all tell-tale signs that someone is not being honest about her eating habits.

Pauline always said no to the biscuits that were passed round at the office coffee break. But every evening she volunteered to work late because it gave her the chance to go through people's desks and steal any food or money she could find. She longed to eat biscuits with the others but due to her eating compulsion she could not let others see her eating. She starved herself all day and by the evening she was so hungry she felt desperate enough to steal anything she could find. One day somebody complained about some missing money and the cleaner got the blame and was dismissed. Pauline felt so guilty she never allowed herself to stay alone late in the office again.

In such cases the person often does not understand why she behaves like this. She does not choose rational actions but blindly follows strange urges that frequently get her into trouble.

WHAT TO DO

Once you begin to notice one or more of these tell-tale signs and start to think that someone you know has a serious eating disorder, what is the best way to handle it?

Breaking the ice, getting a loved one to acknowledge that she is a compulsive eater is probably the most difficult thing of all. A wrong word, the inference that you may be prying, interfering or disapproving can alienate the compulsive eater still further, and any angry confrontation is only likely to send her off on a mammoth binge.

Firstly it is important to realize that this is not some small problem of no great importance. Anyone gripped by an eating disorder is affected in every corner of her life. Food and eating dominate everything she thinks and does. Your actions, each word you say to her, each gesture and implied criticism will be interpreted through her personal filter that relates everything to her body image and her need to eat.

It is pointless trying to reassure her that she is not fat. If a woman is obsessed with her body image she will simply not believe you, or perhaps not even hear what you say.

Getting angry, showing disgust, berating her for her deceit or the stupidity of what she is doing or the pain she is causing others – none of these tactics is likely to have any positive effect. The compulsive eater already knows she is out of control when it comes to food, although she may not yet have realized that she is also out of control of her life. She will only become more helpless and isolated if she feels those close to her have become the enemy, and this can only make her bingeing worse.

On the other hand, you should never ignore what is going on nor go along with it for the sake of peace and quiet. Do not be tempted to help cover up the evidence and thereby appear to be condoning her behaviour. Make it clear that she needs help and that you will be supportive in her attempts to get it.

TRY AND TALK

Be patient and try to get her to talk, but don't be hurt or withdraw your love if she does not seem able to confide in you. Just knowing you care and are supportive will help her in time.

If you know of aspects of her life that are causing her stress you may try talking about them in a positive way. She may need a confidential and sympathetic ear to which she can pour out her doubts and anger about a relationship, her frustrations about her job, or just her disgust about her own body image. But she will not begin to talk until she knows you can be trusted not to criticize her or give away her secret. Try saying things like, 'I love you, but I hate your illness.'

Don't be afraid to express your own feelings about how her problems are affecting your life. You have a right to be angry if her eating disorder is wrecking your life. You have the right to be concerned and worried if someone you love appears to be destroying herself before your eyes. If you feel these things strongly and hold them back it will create further barriers between you; if you expect her to open up to you, you must be prepared to open up to her. Encourage her to seek professional help. She may have already visited her doctor and got nowhere, but it may well be worth trying alternative treatments and/or going to a specialist compulsive eating centre. Meanwhile there are lots of self-help books she could read (including this one and many of those listed in the Recommended Reading chapter).

4

Getting Back in Control: Combating the Emotional Effects of Compulsive Eating

10 Motivation

Once you recognize that you have an eating problem you begin the difficult journey towards getting your eating and your life back under control. The first obstacle on the road is a confusing junction with signposts pointing in all directions. Each one indicates a particular negative trait that is holding you back from a positive, happy life – but which one do you tackle first?

The rest of this book will give you plenty of ideas and advice about developing a more positive attitude. But remember: no advice can be of much use without positive motivation to put it into action.

Motivation means moving, moving out of the rut and onto a forward path. No changes can be made without movement, but getting into action requires both physical and emotional energy. When this is in short supply it can seem easier to stay where you are, in the familiar if painful place you know best.

June had lived all her life in the shadow of an overbearing father. Her mother had long since given up the struggle to stand her own ground and had become a pale shadowy person who burst into tears at the slightest confrontation. June had always avoided making her father angry by not doing things she knew would annoy him, and at 28 she still lived according to this code. June was living the only kind of life she knew, but she was not happy. She came to recognize there was something very wrong, because as the years went by her eating grew more and more out of control. No diet or discipline worked, every attempt at losing weight ended up with more bingeing. She wanted to leave home, but wanting to do it was not enough, she did not know how to go about it. Too many powerful negative influences held her prisoner, smothering her motivation, robbing her of the vital energy she needed to make a move.

June needed the approval of her parents to move out and live her own life, and she certainly was not getting that. Nor did she have her own approval because so many of her thought patterns were rigidly moulded by her family life. She was unable to allow herself to do anything that would upset her parents.

APPROVAL IS MOTIVATION

Usually the strongest driving force behind doing and achieving anything is the seeking of approval. Usually this is the approval of one particular person or group of people, sometimes the approval of the world in general, and sometimes the approval of oneself.

The broad highway along which many compulsive eaters race at breakneck speed is called Low Self-esteem Lane. The root cause of many emotional and social problems in life is a basic lack of self-worth and self-respect. Low self-esteem is so common among those with eating problems it could almost be said that all compulsive eaters are withholding approval of themselves. Not one is pleased with her shape, none is content with her eating habits and few are satisfied with their achievements in life. They think they do not deserve and cannot achieve the better things in life. Entrenched in this belief they settle for second-best or third-rate, label themselves losers and then mould their lives to fit that label. Even if through hard work and determination they have achieved a slim figure, rigid eating control and material success, deep down they do not feel they deserve to be congratulated. The fact that the urge to binge remains strong means this low self-worth still exists, and those who binge do not like themselves for it.

In the case of Eileen, a problem existed but she coped with it by refusing to contact that part of herself which disapproved of her eating habits. Her doctor became concerned for her health and sent her for more specialized help to overcome bulimia, but there was little anyone could do for her.

'I'm not bulimic, I'm just sick after meals,' she said. 'I've done it most of my life and I don't see anything wrong with it.'

Eileen refused to see even the most obvious facts: that her bulimia was undermining both her health and her social life. She was completely unmotivated to change because she had convinced herself there was nothing wrong.

This attitude is very much the exception. Most people with an eating problem are very aware something is wrong, their main problem is knowing how to go about putting things right and overcoming their fear of getting professional help.

BETTER IS BEST

The best motivation for change is a sure knowledge that life will be much better without an eating problem. You will feel so amazingly better about yourself and every part of your life that you will find it difficult to understand how you ever put up with things the way they were.

To get from point A (where you are now) to point B (where you want to be) requires personal change and personal commitment - which requires motivation. Finding strong motivation will be the driving force that not only starts you off in the right direction but keeps you on the road, providing enthusiasm for the smallest daily chores or the largest challenges.

Although some people seem naturally well-motivated, just as some are born to have slim figures, for the majority it takes constant vigilance to keep motivation ticking over. Certain things seem to motivate some people better than others. Tick those on the list below which you feel apply to you.

WHAT MOTIVATES YOU?

- Fear
- Religious beliefs
- The state of the world
- The state of your personal world
- Anger
- Shame
- Love for others
- Being in love
- Revenge
- Habit
- Money
- Power

- The need for approval from:
    your parents
    your children and close family
    your friends
    your colleagues at work
    the world in general
    yourself
- Other reasons

DRIVING FORCES

What you have ticked on the list above can indicate things about the nature of your lifestyle and self-image. Take time to consider these areas carefully. It is here that you are most likely to find clues to the emotional blocks that are contributing to your eating disorder.

Fear

Too often fear holds people back from doing and achieving things, or motivates them to stay where it is safe rather than risk going out and trying to find a better life. When you feel afraid it usually means you are facing some kind of challenge. It is by overcoming challenges that we make progress, though, so try to look on fear as a doorway to the future, not as a brick wall you can't get through. Try reading Susan Jeffers' book *Feel The Fear and Do It Anyway* to get a whole new perspective on fear and how it can motivate you in a positive way.

Religious Beliefs

Your strongly held religious convictions should not be a mere habit nor something that controls and inhibits your self-expression and inflicts guilt. Use your beliefs as a dynamic living force propelling you forward. Sadly, for many people religion does not bring spiritual fulfilment and can drive them towards eating problems as an expression of this inner, spiritual emptiness.

The State of the World

Without people motivated to make changes perhaps the world would not survive. Everyone should feel the need to do something towards helping the starving, preserving the rain forests and reducing pollution, but beware of letting good causes become a replacement for sorting out your own life. It is sometimes easier to devote your life to animals than build good relationships with people. Everything and everyone is equally important in the world.

The State of Your Personal World
If you look at your life, feel the need to make changes and then go out and do it, you are well motivated. By improving yourself and your own environment you automatically affect others around you in a positive way. All change must start from within yourself. This is where your motivation must have its beginning.

Anger
Anger is a very powerful force. It has motivated great changes in the world, not always for the best. If you are sufficiently angry with yourself over your eating habits you will have the motivation to really do something about them, but if anger is your driving force be very careful, this potentially dangerous, destructive emotion must be handled with extreme caution and directed carefully (more about this in the next chapter).

Shame
Shame, like anger, is a double-edged weapon. If you feel ashamed of the way you are living your life you can use this as a creative driving force to motivate change for the better. But beware of allowing that shame to turn inwards and fester or it will have the reverse effect.

Love for Others
Relatively few people are motivated purely by love for others. The exceptional, such as Mother Teresa, can change the world through unconditional love, but everyone is free to try in his or her own way.

A compulsive eating habit affects not just the person with the problem but all those who have to live with her. It can disrupt or destroy relationships and bring endless grief to parents, partners, siblings, children and friends. If that person cares deeply for those close to her she has something important to motivate her to seek help in getting her eating and her life back under control. Nobody who truly and unconditionally loves other people can inflict this on them. People who are capable of feeling genuine love for others have a wonderful tool at their disposal for getting back in control of their eating and their lives.

Being in Love

Falling in love, floating on clouds of romance can be an instant cure for every trouble known to humanity. Eating problems melt away when Cupid fires his dart ~ the only problem is that such heady stuff cannot last. Sooner or later passion mellows into a loving relationship or ends with pain and regrets, and that is when an old eating problem may rear its ugly head again.

Perhaps finding the right partner and starting a new life are all that some compulsive eaters need to get rid of their eating problem for good ~ certainly if loneliness and feeling unloved were the root causes. Compulsive eating fades into a memory of a difficult phase of life that is now gone for good. But if you have not come to terms with underlying emotional problems, new problems may begin to arise as the relationship settles down. Perhaps the strain of giving up work and becoming a mother, financial struggles or problems with in-laws will spark the old urge to binge. Your eating habits can degenerate gradually until you are back in the starve/binge cycle just like in the old days before you fell in love.

The greatest danger is when a love affair goes wrong. In the terrible pain of breaking up or realizing the object of your adoration does indeed have feet of clay, the first thing you reach for may be food. Severe bingeing being the expression of all your unhappiness.

Revenge

It is difficult to turn revenge into a positive weapon, although it can be done. If someone were to hurt you by making unkind remarks about your appearance, you could be motivated to get your own back by improving your looks and figure so much that you end up looking more attractive than that person. Revenge is generally destructive, however: if you try to get even with someone you believe has hurt you, you often end up getting hurt yourself in the process. Too often the urge for revenge gets turned inward in the form of punishing yourself with bingeing and bulimia.

The Need for Approval from Others

This is the incentive most likely to motivate you to make changes that need to be made, take actions that need to be taken. We all want our parents to be proud of us, our children to respect us, our colleagues to admire us and our friends to like us, and we are prepared to go to great lengths to achieve this. What other reason is there for the great secrecy surrounding a binge, but the fear of attracting disapproval?

It is a mistake to think people cannot approve of you unless you are perfect in every way. The appearance of perfection often puts people off. For example, it can be difficult for someone with an eating problem to talk to a counsellor who is slim, happily married and well organized; she will relate better to someone who has battle scars from the same war she is now engaged in. Don't be afraid to show your human face. People find it reassuring and lovable and will approve of you even more for your courage in facing up to your problems.

Habit

This is one of the most powerful reasons for doing anything, but is it really a motivator? It is easy to slip into bad habits and then carry on living your life that way because you 'always' have. Bingeing is a bad habit. Consider carefully whether your habits are holding you back rather than urging you forward.

SELF-APPROVAL

The one thing that will truly motivate you to improve your life is approving of yourself, respecting and loving yourself - faults, weaknesses, binges and all - and caring about yourself enough to reward yourself with happiness and peace of mind.

DON'T BE FOOLED

Never fall into the trap of believing other people are better motivated than you. Maybe they are better at *appearing* well motivated, but probably they are struggling just as hard as you. As an outsider you only see the things that other people achieve, you do not know about their failures, their secret disappointments, or the standards they set themselves.

How many people know you have an eating problem? Using this gauge, is it likely that you know just how many of your acquaintances and colleagues are struggling against the same odds – and possibly envying your apparent lack of problems? Assume life is as difficult for the rest of the world as it is for you; if others seem to be making a go of it, so can you.

After an eating disorders workshop the organizer was feeling pleased with herself because it had gone well. Everyone seemed to benefit from it, and the next day the phone started to ring with thank-yous for a constructive day. 'I enjoyed the workshop but I felt so inferior, everyone else was so well dressed, so communicative, and they all had much better jobs than me,' said the first caller. Then, to the organizer's amazement, each participant in turn called with the same story. Each had been summing up the others and comparing herself unfavourably to everyone else. The workshop had been a get-together of women with low self-esteem, each hiding behind a veneer of confidence and sophistication.

Everyone has inner fears and doubts. You are not alone.

SABOTAGE

The minefield through which all motivation has to steer is called sabotage. Logically you would think that all people try to do the best for themselves and are working towards making their lives as easy and successful as possible. There are few people who don't at some time sabotage their own best efforts. There is a seed of self-destruction in each of us that makes us do things that are against our best interests. None of us is perfect.

Suggestion: Accept from the outset that you are likely at some point to sabotage your most determined and motivated efforts to get your eating under control. It will help if you accept this fact now so that you recognize it for what it is when it happens. You will then be able to learn to live with it and won't let it destroy your motivation.

Time and again someone with an eating problem will set out on the road to recovery with a sensible eating plan and positive mental approach, then she will deliberately put herself into a situation which she knows will lead to bingeing – such as crash dieting before Christmas – and feel she has failed.

Probably the easiest form of sabotage is 'I'll just have one, it won't do me any harm.' Just one drink often leads to another and another. Just one biscuit means two more the next day and a binge the day after. For many compulsive eaters there is no such thing as 'just one', and until you are fully back in control of your eating you cannot handle even 'just one'.

Another way of sabotaging is by failing to live up to your own expectations or by setting yourself unrealistic goals. Sheila arranged to go to an exercise class with her friend each week. She went twice, but on the third week she didn't bother. She left her friend to go on her own while she stayed at home, got bored and started to binge. Because she had missed one she felt she had failed and therefore didn't go again.

Then there are the situations where you are not really giving yourself a chance. Sophie bought her grandmother a birthday present of a box of chocolates – but she bought it a month before her grandmother's birthday! Of course long before the day came round Sophie had eaten all the chocolates herself.

Pay-Offs

When you find yourself sabotaging your best efforts – and sooner or later you will – you have to ask yourself why you are doing it. Are the pay-offs for having an eating disorder, being overweight, feeling a failure actually worth the anguish of being drawn back into the bingeing cycle?

Karen said over and over again that she longed to get her eating under control, but every time she began to make progress something happened and it all fell apart. Her excuses for slipping back into her old ways of eating appeared weak, and when strongly challenged she admitted that she felt safer sticking with her eating problem. 'People would expect more from me if I hadn't got an eating problem,' she said. For Karen the battle had to start elsewhere: until she could discover greater self-confidence and self-esteem she would endlessly sabotage anything that improved her eating habits.

When bingeing provides such a comfortable excuse for so many things – from failing an exam to failing in a marriage – why not stick with the bingeing instead of facing up to the real reason for failure? The answer goes back to self-approval. You must take the first steps towards loving and approving of yourself. You deserve the best in life - believe this and you will truly be motivated to sort out your life and get your eating back under control.

11 Negative Emotions

Just as motivation can direct us in a positive or negative way, other strong emotions that influence how we feel about ourselves and how we react to events in our lives can be double-edged. Life can become tough and unhappy when we allow positive emotions to become negative – and by the same token the key to a better life lies in transforming negative feelings to positive ones.

When making the decision to overcome an eating disorder there is no room for negative emotions. They have to be recognized and tackled as part of your plan for getting back in control of your eating and your life. Discarding the junk thoughts from your mind is even more essential than throwing out the junk food from your diet. You are learning how to be the one in control. You no longer need the boost you get from a bout of self-pity or a box of chocolates. You are being offered better ways to feel good in mind and body.

Listed below are some commonly felt emotions which usually take a negative form and so drag people down. How much do these emotions feature in your life?

The answers you have given are personal to you. By studying them further you can learn something more about how you view the world. (Fear and depression are such huge topics for the compulsive eater, however, that each has been given a chapter to itself – Chapters 12 and 13 respectively.)

ANGER

Maybe you think the positive side of anger is self-control, or perhaps you see it as tolerance or patience, or maybe as silence. Each of these may be right for you, but each of them has its own positive and negative element.

If you know you are a person who flies off the handle too quickly and are aware this is not doing your relationships and social life any

Table 16 COMMONLY FELT EMOTIONS

	Often	Sometimes	Never
Anger	☐	☐	☐
Resentment	☐	☐	☐
Guilt	☐	☐	☐
Jealousy	☐	☐	☐
Hate	☐	☐	☐
Boredom	☐	☐	☐
Fear	☐	☐	☐
Depression	☐	☐	☐

good, it may be a very positive thing to develop more tolerance and self-control. On the other hand if you are the sort of person who never expresses anger outwardly, it could be an extremely positive experience for you to be very angry, to shout and yell and let it all out. It's not easy to reverse long-held habits, but counsellors and workshops exist to help you release these blocks in a safe way if you feel unable to do it alone.

Ellen was an angry person. She was angry about the state of the world, angry about cruelty to animals, angry at the local council. She was also angry at her parents for allowing her to be born and angry at her husband because they lived in a fourth-floor flat. She got angry when the baby cried. She got angry when her husband was late for a meal. Ellen was always getting angry, and when she was angry she ended up feeling guilty and then she started to binge.

Before Ellen could get back in control of her eating she had to come to terms with a lot of her anger. She was asked to write a list of all the things that made her angry in a week. It was a long list. Then she was asked to divide that list into things she could do something about and things she could do nothing about. At first she was tempted to put everything on the second list, but with some help from others she started to think how she could take positive action. That was how she changed her life.

She became an active member of Friends of the Earth and an animal protection society. She wrote letters and led campaigns to try and put right some of the injustices of the world she felt so passionately about. With more outside interests she was less angry at home, nicer to live with and less driven to binge.

Gradually she found she was able to transfer more things from the second list to the first. Those things she had once thought impossible, like keeping her patience with the children, began to seem within her grasp as her confidence grew. She started on longer-term projects that would greatly improve the quality of her life, like saving to buy a house with a garden. On the day the family moved home Ellen found she was no longer angry about having been born. Nor was she a compulsive eater any more.

On the surface Sylvie appeared to be a very different person from the raging Ellen. Nobody had ever seen Sylvie even mildly ruffled, much less angry. No matter what happened Sylvie would always smile and say the right thing, because that was the way she had been brought up. Her mother had instilled in Sylvie the importance of never showing her anger or annoyance. Others would treat her better if she was always nice to them, she'd been told.

Like Ellen, however, Sylvie had an eating problem. Deep down there were many things that Sylvie was not happy about, but she did not know how to let those dissatisfactions out in healthy anger. They stayed trapped inside, and she would smother them with food. For Sylvie, counselling and workshops helped her to understand that it was acceptable for her to feel anger and to express it in an appropriate way.

Misdirected anger is another negative trait that causes much bad feeling in relationships. A man under a lot of pressure at work may come home and take out his frustrations by being short-tempered with the children. Here the anger is not being fully suppressed yet it is not being directed in a positive way. This man would be better off taking out his pent-up emotions on the squash court, or better still sorting out a better working atmosphere at the office.

RESENTMENT

Bottled-up anger leads to resentment. When a grievance is not aired but brooded over it grows out of all proportion. There is rarely a positive side to this sort of situation, although it may lead to confrontation if that is what is needed to clear the air. Provided this confrontation is undertaken in a spirit of positive progress all may yet be well; otherwise it could end in recriminations on both sides, making things worse.

Letting go can be a positive experience, whether by expressing your anger (again, in an appropriate way) or simply trying to keep in perspective the thing that has upset you. All those brooding thoughts send out long roots that become entangled in every part of your life - it may even help to try and visualize your resentment as a tenacious weed that you have to pull out bit by bit. See yourself putting each piece in a bag and throwing it away or burning it on a bonfire so it can never return. Slowly you will feel yourself free of this destructive emotion. Recognize that you may have a tendency to overanalyse things or that sometimes you are worrying unnecessarily.

GUILT

A jury is asked to pronounce a verdict of guilty or not guilty on a defendant, having decided whether he has committed or is innocent of a particular crime.

In everyday life, questions of guilt or innocence are rarely so clear cut, yet when we act as our own jury we are the harshest judge of all. We can feel very guilty over small things, or guilt can grow and grow as time goes by, nurtured by too much self-absorption and too great a willingness to blame ourselves for all the troubles in the world. The person who has done nothing wrong can drown in guilt while others can leave a trail of wreckage in their wake and not feel bad about it at all.

A guilt trip can be a great indulgence, a mammoth wallow in the negative that is almost enjoyable yet at the same time hugely self-destructive. Guilt is only positive if it pricks you to put right what you know to be wrong. If your guilt about bingeing spurs you on to sort out your eating habits, the end result will be positive. However, too many people are so negative about their eating the guilt itself promotes further bingeing, which promotes further guilt. They are trapped in a downward spiral.

When it comes to feeling guilty about your eating habits it is yourself you have to answer to. This is particularly true if no one else even knows you have an eating problem. If you feel guilty about eating a biscuit it is because you have broken the rules about what you may and may not eat. But who made those rules? You made them and you are free to break them or adjust them to suit yourself, so why feel guilty?

THE BURDEN OF GUILT

How heavy is your load of guilt? Answer the following questions:

1. Have I the right to time to myself each day?
2. Have I the right to ask for what I need and to have my needs met?
3. Have I the right to be treated with respect?
4. Have I the right to express my own feelings and opinions?
5. Have I the right to set my own values without seeking the approval of others?
6. Have I the right to make mistakes?
7. Have I the right to change my mind?
8. Have I the right to refuse to take on board other people's problems?
9. Have I the right to ask for help?
10. Have I the right to pamper myself?

How many of the above questions made you cringe inwardly with guilt as you read them? Did a little voice keep murmuring negative ideas in your ear, such as 'You are always bingeing so you have no right to be treated with respect' or 'You are a strong woman, you have no right to ask for help.' If you were able to answer yes to any or all of the above questions, read them again and this time add after each one the words '. . . and not feel guilty.' You may discover a subtle difference as you realize you are finding it hard to allow yourself these basic human rights.

Let's rewrite all this in a positive way. Copy the following 'Guilt-free Charter' and put it up where you can read it every day.

I have the right to take time for myself each day.
I have the right to ask for what I need.
I have the right to have my needs met.

I have the right to be treated with respect.
I have the right to express my own feelings and opinions.
I have the right to hold my own values.
I have the right to make mistakes.
I have the right to change my mind.
I have the right to refuse to take on a responsibility.
I have the right to ask for help.
I have the right to pamper myself.
 Without feeling guilty

JEALOUSY

Jealousy often has its roots in childhood, starting with feelings of
envy towards a brother or sister who seems to be more clever, better-
looking or more loved. In later life this can take the form of seeing
everybody else as perfect and only yourself as having faults, which
is an expression of low self-esteem.

To assume you are the only person in the world with problems
is not only totally false but another self-indulgence. Everyone has
problems – maybe not the same problems as you, but certainly
other people's problems seem just as huge to them. The irony of
such a situation is that others may well be secretly jealous of you – as
discussed earlier it is all to do with image and projection.

Jealousy rarely has much of a foundation in reality. It is easy, for
example, to be jealous of someone who is very rich without
considering the other aspects of his life. Alternatively you may feel
jealous of someone who has a good figure without being prepared
yourself to put in the hours of exercise and the programme of
sensible eating that helps that person maintain her looks.

Sally-Ann started going to exercise classes and envied the instructor her
vitality and good figure. She decided to train as an instructor herself.
Soon business was so good she was able to give up her office job and
devote herself entirely to teaching. She worked hard, leading 12 classes
a week and working out in the gym to keep herself in top form. She
enjoyed her new life and she looked wonderful. She had used her
jealousy positively, to achieve that which she'd coveted.

Jealousy is a far more commonly felt negative emotion than many people realize. If, for example, someone seems to dislike you for no obvious reason, if you have always tried to be pleasant with him and have never done anything to upset him but he continues to treat you badly, consider whether he might be feeling jealous of you. It may come as a surprise to realize that someone envies you, probably for something you take for granted. Perhaps he wishes he had the job you are doing (which you may find unfulfilling!), or that he were married to a spouse as nice as yours (even though you are not really satisfied with your marriage). If you find his reasons for envying you unrealistic, take a better look at *your* reasons for envying other people.

HATE

Although hate is perhaps the most powerful negative emotion, it is not often found in everyday life. The thing we call hate is more likely to be something else. For example, if you say you hate dogs you may in fact be afraid of dogs, or if you say you hate your sister perhaps it is nearer the truth that you are jealous of her. Few people really hate anything or anyone. Hatred and fear are often confused.

Siobhan has never forgotten her old school teacher Miss Hamilton. All the girls in her class agreed that they hated Miss Hamilton because she was very strict and never let anyone get away with not doing her homework. What the girls in the class were feeling was really fear rather than hatred, or resentment of Miss Hamilton's strict authority. But it was Miss Hamilton who realized Siobhan had problems at home and discovered that she binged to comfort herself then made herself sick in the school toilets. It was this 'dragon' of a schoolmistress who arranged for Siobhan to get professional help with her bulimia and her problems at home. In later life Siobhan saw all of Miss Hamilton's actions as aimed at getting the best for her pupils; she often had reason to thank Miss Hamilton for this. She warned her own children about making negative judgements about people, especially school teachers.

'Where there is hatred let me sow love,' said St Francis of Assisi. None of us is a saint, but we can all try to see feelings of hatred as a challenge to learn something about thinking and feeling love. It is easy to love a fluffy kitten, until it turns and scratches you. That is the moment when you have the opportunity to act in a positive way or sink into the negative. Gently scold the kitten, understand he did not deliberately draw blood, and he may learn not to scratch in future. Hit him and throw him out of the house and he may learn to match aggression with aggression. It is exactly the same with human relationships. If a bad situation arises you have the choice of reacting positively or negatively. You can respond with understanding and compassion so you can hopefully build enough bridges to exist in peace together, or you can let emotions such as hate, fear, jealousy and resentment drag you down into a situation that can bring nothing but misery for everyone.

BOREDOM

Another blind alley that many people are tempted down is labelled boredom. It is such an easy route downhill, then one day you find you no longer have the energy or motivation to clamber back up. You are stuck at the bottom of the pit. If there is plenty of food down there in no time at all you are eating and thinking about food instead of looking around for a way out. Eating takes over, swiftly followed by guilt, low self-esteem, lethargy and all the familiar baddies that lurk at the bottom of Boredom Hill.

Martin is a perfect example of someone whose main problem in life was boredom, although he didn't recognize it at first and binged as a way of escaping the negative lifestyle he had slipped into.

He had always had a problem with food. He was overweight as a child and his mother tended to worry about his eating habits. Naturally shy, he found it difficult to form close relationships and ended up living in a bed-sit. He would get home from work, switch on the television, and from then on the evening was a succession of snacks in front of the screen. His only social life was an evening at the pub. Although this was a break from snacking in front of the television, his mates were heavy drinkers and he would find himself trying to keep up with them pint for pint.

The best thing that happened to Martin was his television breaking down. He took it into the repair shop but they said it would take a couple of weeks to repair. Suddenly Martin discovered whole empty areas in his life which he had been filling up with food and television.

Grasping the moment, he listened to good advice and committed himself to finding some outside interests. An assertion training weekend got him off to an excellent start. The next week he enrolled in an adult education class to learn French conversation. On Saturday night he spent an enjoyable evening with his friends drinking low-calorie soft drinks and not feeling embarrassed about it. He quickly discovered he was losing weight and treated himself to some new clothes. When the television repair man telephoned to say his set was ready Martin was not sure he wanted it back. He had learned so much about himself and how he wanted to live his life that he now only turns the television on if there is a programme he really wants to watch.

EXCUSES

If you feel your life is in a rut, decide now that *you* can *change* your situation. Everyone can come up with a list of excuses for not doing something more exciting than the usual boring routine, but there is an answer for every excuse if you are prepared to look again. (I have written about this more extensively in my book *Excuses Won't Cure You.*) Some favourite excuses (and suggestions for turning them around) include:

- My job is boring.
  Suggestion: Decide *why* you are bored by it and, if necessary, go to your boss and ask for more responsibility – or look for a new job.
- It's difficult to find a job these days.
  Suggestion: Go to an evening class and train in a new skill.
- I haven't got enough money to go out.
  Suggestion: Balance up the cost of a seat at the cinema against the price of food for an evening at home bingeing.
- I'm frightened to go out after dark.
  Suggestion: Invite some people round, or balance up the cost of a taxi to go see some friends against bingeing.
- I haven't got any friends.
  Suggestion: Maybe your obsession with food and weight has made you such a difficult person that they are making excuses to avoid you. Try taking a real interest in other people and the things they care about.

- I'm too tired at the end of the day.
  Suggestion: There's nothing more tiring than being bored. If you make the effort to start doing something you are likely to feel more lively and energetic.
- My partner won't let me.
  Suggestion: A definite case for assertiveness training!

The inertia of boredom feeds on itself. The less you do, the less you seem able to achieve. Doing nothing is an occupation that expands to fill all the time you allow it. It suffocates ambition, ideas and motivation. People who lead a busy life always find time to squeeze in something extra, but those with an empty, boring life never seem to have a moment to spare for positive action. Don't let this negativity overwhelm you!

BE POSITIVE

Every life has its downs. Every human being faces bad patches. There is no such thing as a trouble-free existence. What *can* be achieved by anyone, however, is the inner strength and self-respect to ride out the bad times and survive anything and everything that life may throw at you.

If you cannot treat others in a positive way it is unlikely you can be positive about yourself. How many of the negative emotions mentioned in this chapter do you apply to yourself every day, especially in respect of your eating?

Most compulsive eaters experience the full range of negative emotions. They are angry with themselves for not having control over their eating, they resent their inability to lose weight, to stop bingeing, to escape from the eating trap. Every time it all goes wrong their guilt grows. Guilt about eating one biscuit is the reason for eating the rest of the packet. They can end up hating themselves and the dull, empty life that has driven them to this level of degradation and despair.

Begin to tackle your negative emotions one by one. Isolate one trait and resolve to work on it by being *positive*. An example:

It is ten in the morning and you have just eaten a bar of chocolate. You feel guilty because you promised yourself you would not eat any sweets this week. You feel so guilty, in fact, you are in danger of abandoning sensible eating and bingeing for the rest of the day. This is the point at which you must tackle the guilt.

What you *should* do is say to yourself that just because you have eaten the 'wrong' thing in the morning is no reason to continue this trend throughout the day. Don't make yourself promises about what you can and cannot do. You may be setting yourself up for failure.

Think: 'Yes, I feel guilty but I don't need to.'

'Yes, I ate chocolate when I promised myself I would not, but the world has not come to an end, it's not that important. Just because I've started doesn't mean I have to carry on.'

'I am going to be positive about this situation and start the day over again with a new resolution not to eat any more sweets.'

By talking to yourself in this way you are not only being honest with yourself, you are refusing to be dragged down by habitual negative responses. Often when people are able to take this on it is a sign that they are beginning to get better.

Stop, look and listen. Stop your headlong gallop into negative indulgence, *look* at yourself and *listen* to what your body is telling you. Perhaps it is saying 'I need food' because you skipped breakfast.

Get into the habit of recognizing negative thoughts; every time you are aware of one popping into your head take hold of it deliberately and find a positive way of expressing that same idea. This is very difficult at first but, as with everything, in time it can become a habit and you will be able to do it automatically.

Begin with the following – and feel free to add plenty of your own:

- I can't do that → becomes → *I find that difficult but I will try.*
- *I can't stick to my eating plan because I haven't time to cook* → becomes → *I can choose something to eat that only involves opening a tin.*
- *I always binge on Sundays* → becomes → *I know I have been tempted to binge on Sundays in the past, so this Sunday I am planning to go out on a special trip so I will not be at home all day thinking about eating.*

12 Fear

Of all the emotions that dominate the life of a compulsive eater, fear is probably the greatest and the most difficult to overcome.

Fear can stifle motivation but it can also be a great motivator, the reason for doing – or not doing – almost anything in life. If fear influences your behaviour and thought patterns, learn to have a positive relationship with it. Make sure your fear is working for you, driving you forward towards success, not crippling your efforts to get back in control.

We learn fear, we are not born with it. Bad experiences or advice meant kindly teach us that there are things to be feared. A mother who tells her child not to talk to strangers (necessary if she is to keep her child safe from molesters and kidnappers) is not only protecting her child from possible harm but also instilling a fear of other people.

Fear of food also begins at an early age – 'If you don't eat your dinner you won't grow up to be healthy' states one message, then later on there comes a contrary message: 'If you eat that you will get fat.' The media have plenty of fear-inspiring messages about food as well: in the endless reporting of latest research they manage to put across panic messages about almost any food, which the consumer is likely to only half-understand. For instance:

- Butter gives you heart attacks.
- Margarine gives you cancer.
- Eggs contain poisonous bacteria.
- Cheese gives you headaches.
- Tuna contains mercury.
- Alcohol destroys your liver.
- Chocolate is addictive.

The list continues until the consumer is afraid to eat anything. Then the 'experts' discuss and analyse the psychological side of eating and a further set of taboos hits the consumer, such as:

- Dieting makes you fat.
- Successful people are slim.
- Fat people are figures of fun.
- Eating the wrong foods is dangerous.
- Eating too much is dangerous.
- Eating too little is dangerous.

With so much conflicting information it is hardly surprising that not only does food become associated with fear, but before long fear becomes associated with food. One day you realize that your fear of speaking to strangers is associated with your negative eating habits: you binge when you know you have to meet people you don't know.

Alice made a start on the Eating Plan and signed up for a workshop where she would meet other people with eating problems. The more she thought about going the more nervous she became. The night before she hardly slept at all, then when she did drop off she overslept and rushed out with no breakfast. At the station she began to feel sick, bought a bag of doughnuts and ate them all, then went back home for a binge. She never got to the workshop.

The negative emotions that hold you back become compounded by fear of those negative emotions. The states of mind that then develop include:

- fear of showing anger
- fear of being rejected
- fear of hurting somebody
- fear of feeling guilty
- fear of boring people
- fear of not being loved
- fear of failure
- fear of being hurt
- fear of loneliness
- fear of ridicule

The greatest fear that dominates the life of almost anyone with an eating disorder, however, is the *fear of getting fat*.

This fear is present every time a compulsive eater or bulimic eats, every time she makes herself sick, every time she starves herself. But what is there to fear about being fat, unless you are going to become so grossly obese that you wreck your health and die?

First of all, it is important to analyse what you mean by 'getting fat'. If you have an eating problem this probably means a shape and weight that the world in general would consider quite acceptable but that *you* consider unacceptable.

Secondly it is necessary to analyse exactly what your fear is. If, for example, you have set yourself a target weight of nine stone and are afraid to eat any quantity of food which you think might lead to your going over that nine-stone limit, what is it you fear would happen if you weighed nine stone plus?

If you were told that you were always going to be a stone heavier than your ideal weight and nothing could ever change that, how would you react? Would you come up with one of these responses?:

- I would commit suicide.
- I would still carry on trying to lose weight regardless.
- I would move abroad because people there wouldn't know I had put on weight.
- I would accept it as long as I was promised it was only one stone.
- I would resign myself to being a stone heavier.

Or would you have your own, different reaction to such a situation? The fact is that many people who are locked in the diet/binge weight battle do go on for years never quite reaching their 'ideal' weight. They are living with the hypothetical situation described above *all the time*, but refuse to recognize it and are making their lives miserable. If you are in reality living with being just a few pounds over, why can't you accept it and concentrate on something more positive in your life?

GETTING BOXED IN

Fear is usually at the root of an inability to face up to reality. Fear makes it difficult to make changes, even changes for the better. Fear is a crippling and suffocating force that limits everyday life. It is not only major phobias that have a devastating effect, often just small fears work insidiously to undermine our quality of life. When food and eating are a problem, fear can set off an eating binge. In this way, eating itself becomes something to be feared. The compulsive eater lives in dread of the next binge, and the circle tightens as the problem grows.

Elaine had lived with her eating problems for so long that she had lost touch with reality when it came to dealing with food. Her whole life revolved around her terror of putting on weight. Everything she did was considered in relationship to how it would affect her weight. She never went out socially in case she was expected to eat, she could never plan anything more than a few hours in advance in case she was overcome by the urge to binge and the need to vomit.

Certain foods terrified her. She dreaded being alone with a loaf of bread – she knew she would not be able to resist eating it all. She avoided anything she feared might have the minutest drop of fat in it, believing it would add pounds to her weight.

She desperately wanted help to overcome her bulimia but she was unable to give up the habit of making herself sick after nearly every meal because she was so frightened she would put on weight.

Like so many other negative states, fear boxes people into a tighter and tighter corner. The only escape is to fight back – but the compulsive eater is not seriously thinking about escaping. She is only concerned about her eating habits, because while she is bingeing she can forget temporarily all the things that frighten her. When you are overwhelmed with life problems and negative emotions, positive things like creativity become squashed and stifled, things such as self-expression are denied as anger, fear, resentment and lethargy expand, allowing less and less room for positive emotions and personal fulfilment.

To overcome these problems you need to learn to take emotional risks and, gradually as your confidence builds, this will help you to conquer the psychological desire to binge. The assertiveness exercise on page 216 is a useful starting point for rediscovering your creativity.

A COURAGEOUS QUEST

As every great warrior learns, the way to conquer fear is to tackle it face-to-face. Like Theseus finding his way through the maze to slay the Minotaur, or Sir Lancelot riding through perilous forests to seek out the Black Knight, you can't afford to sit indoors trying to avoid your fears – you have to go out and confront them. You have to take risks.

You will never know if you can get your eating under control until you take steps to improve your eating habits and come to terms with the problems that are making you binge. It is of course much easier to carry on in familiar habits. It takes energy to change and it takes courage to overcome the fear of change.

The most frightening feeling of all is the feeling of being quite helpless. That is the state you are likely to be in if eating and food are totally dominating your life. No matter how frightening it may feel to contemplate what must be done to overcome your eating habits, as long as you are doing something positive to improve your life you will be able to handle the fear because you will be facing up to it actively rather than sitting back passively and letting it swamp you.

WHAT COULD BE WORSE?

Perhaps you are stuck in a bad relationship because you are afraid of being alone. If things are really that bad now, how could they be worse when you have only yourself to be responsible for and have the opportunity to build a new life for yourself?

Perhaps you are staying at home every evening because you are shy and afraid people will ignore you. If that were to happen would it really be any worse than being home alone? It is likely that you would find someone to talk to if you were prepared to put on a brave face. Practise developing a sociable, outgoing image to project on when you are with people – in time that image could be the real you.

Of course, plunging straight into parties, pubs and such social venues is the difficult way of going about overcoming shyness. Why not do things the easy way and join an appropriate evening class where the pressure to socialize is reduced and you can get to know people with similar interests in a slower, more relaxed way?

A Brave Approach

Beware of casting yourself in the role of fearful victim. Do you see yourself as the nervous antelope starting at every shadow or as the powerful lion stalking through the grass? Do you feel life is your enemy, ready to knock you back every time you try to take a step forward, or can you take responsibility for your actions and their consequences?

The clue is whether you feel you are in control of your life or whether someone or something is in control of you. Anyone who has an eating disorder is likely to feel that at least one part of her life is definitely not under control.

Don't blame anyone or anything for this. You may be in the habit of saying 'It's my father's fault that I find it difficult to relate to men,' or 'It's my mother's fault that I am fat.' Maybe they once had a great influence over your life, but now you are an adult you must take the power and responsibility into your own hands. Don't be afraid to take control of those things that others once controlled for you.

Outside Influences

Fear is very contagious; one fearful person can easily infect others. Learn to recognize other people's fears and try to prevent them rubbing off on you.

Courage is equally contagious. The inspiration to overcome problems can come from others. It can empower you to adopt your own positive attitude, which in turn will influence others. It is therefore important to try and seek out people who have ~ or appear to have ~ courage to face life head on. You will find that the company of well-motivated people will alter your own perspectives of what you believe you can achieve. Equally, avoid those who are gloomy and negative. They have nothing to offer you and are doomed to a lonely, miserable life because that is what they are creating for themselves. You do not need them.

HAVE A GO

You never know what you can do until you try. You can change your life at any moment, as soon as you find the courage to change your attitude. Sometimes it takes a prod from fate to initiate that change. Be ready to take advantage of whatever life offers. Nobody has a life that is totally free from trouble and setbacks. It is not the number of setbacks that matters but the way you handle them. If you are prepared to go out and look life full in the face you are likely to have to deal with more difficult situations than the person who sits safely at home. The difference is that the person who goes out and has a go usually finds she can handle it. In time she discovers that there is nothing she cannot cope with because when she feels afraid she knows how to overcome her fear. Fear is usually the first and highest hurdle. Clear that one and all the others seem less daunting.

Our minds can play very unkind tricks on us. As soon as you consider doing something that you believe is difficult your brain puts all sorts of extra ideas into your head. For example:

- Main Thought: I have been invited to meet my boyfriend's parents.
  Extra Thoughts: What if they don't like me? *Fear*
  What if I say the wrong thing? *Fear*
  What if they don't know I am a vegetarian and expect me to eat meat? *Fear*
  What if I spill my tea on the carpet? *Fear*
  What if they have heard about my eating problems? *Fear*

Lorraine always binged the day before she had to go and visit her parents-in-law. They lived a long way away and she rarely saw them, but they were able to inspire such terror in her that the thought of the twice-yearly visits turned her into a shaking, bingeing wreck. They were always polite to her but she felt awkward and uneasy in their large expensive house where the chairs looked too clean to sit on and the plates too fine to eat off. She always managed to say something that shocked and dismayed them and to break a glass or knock over a plant pot even though she rarely had such accidents at home. Inevitably she and her husband would have a blazing row before the weekend was over.

Because Lorraine was a rather unconventional person and her in-laws were extremely straight-laced and respectable, she had never been able to create any kind of relationship with them. In her mind they grew into ogres of Victorian discipline and morality who threatened to tear her apart and wreck her marriage. Her fear had grown out of all proportion, so distorting her personality that when she was with them this well-meaning, ordinary, conventional couple found her a complete mystery; they felt threatened and afraid of her and fearful for their son, who seemed to have married a walking disaster. It was a classic example of negative states of anxiety and fear feeding each other. Before things could be resolved one party would have to break out of the set pattern and reach out courageously to understand the other. Sadly this never happened because Lorraine and her husband split up. Her in-laws were left to console their son with 'It's for the best' and 'She wasn't really your type' while Lorraine contested bitterly for many years that her parents-in-law had broken up her marriage.

BE PREPARED

If most of what we fear exists only in our minds, then our minds are where we have to fight the fiercest battles against fear. Thankfully, not many people actually get to experience the terror of dangling over a pit full of poisonous snakes or looking down the barrel of a loaded gun, yet social situations and lifestyle stresses – how to face a difficult colleague, how to stand up to an overbearing parent, how to go out and enjoy life – are not less debilitating or challenging, just of a different character.

When a lorry skidded out of control near a school, Verity rushed in without a thought for her own safety and saved a baby from being crushed in its pram. She was awarded a medal for her bravery, but thought it ironic that she still did not dare tell her mother not to knit her another cardigan for Christmas. Fear and bravery often have little to do with the actual severity of the challenge being faced. They are more to do with each individual's personal vulnerabilities.

It is important to be honest with yourself and understand which situations make you feel afraid and where the boundaries of your fear are drawn. Then you can begin to work on pushing forward those boundaries.

For every situation that inspires fear in some people, the opposite state is equally fearful for others. This would further support the idea that it is not the situation itself that creates the fear but the attitude of the person considering it. Any situation can lead to bingeing in the compulsive eater if it happens to ring her particular bell. In more serious cases both sides of a question can be equally stressful, as in the case of a mother who does not feel she can cope with her teenage children yet dreads the day they will leave home.

FOOD FEARS

There are certain fears that affect compulsive eaters in particular.

Eating in public can be very difficult for those who are locked in a battle with themselves over what they do and do not allow themselves to eat. They feel guilty about eating and dread others seeing them eat. They think, 'People will think I am greedy' and may either avoid eating with others absolutely or may eat only small amounts of low-calorie food in public (and then go home alone for a large binge).

Shopping is another thing many compulsive eaters fear. Large supermarkets can even bring on panic attacks. Faced with so much food and such a huge choice the compulsive eater feels totally overwhelmed; if the shop is crowded and there is no daylight she can feel trapped and panicky.

There are certain guidelines that can be followed to make shopping easier:

1. Never go shopping straight from work when you are probably hungry, your blood sugar levels are dropping and you may well be feeling tired.
2. Don't wander aimlessly round the shop. Make a list before you leave home; if you know the shop well write things down in the order in which you will find them on the shelves. Walk in, go straight round the shop collecting only the things on your list, then go straight to the checkout.
3. Choose a checkout that has not got a display of sweets next to it. If this is not possible try taking something to read or someone to talk to while you are waiting in the queue. Alternatively, write to your regular supermarket's head office stating that you object to their policy and are withdrawing your custom for this reason.
4. Get your partner or someone else to do the shopping for you.

FACING FEAR

The action needed to overcome a particular fear may well depend on the nature of the fear itself. There follow a few examples. If your personal phobia is not here, use the techniques suggested to analyse your problem and turn it around in a similar way.

FEAR OF A PARTICULAR PERSON

A woman who stays in a violent relationship is usually more afraid of leaving than of being physically beaten.

A refuge or shelter, social worker or counsellor should be able to provide the emotional support she needs to overcome the fear of living and surviving alone. If it is mental cruelty that makes the other party someone to be feared, assertion training and learning to love and respect herself will teach her to see that she does not need to live in fear.

FEAR OF PEOPLE IN GENERAL

For some people the faceless crowd can be terrifying, even though they can handle one-on-one relationships.

Any confidence-building exercise or workshop will help dispel this fear of the unknown. Meanwhile the best thing to do is go out and mix with people as much as possible – you'll discover they are rarely anything to be feared.

FEAR OF LONELINESS

Those who fear being lonely are often lonely already, what they really fear is their loneliness getting worse. People who spend a lot of time in crowded pubs or with people they do not really care about because they dread being alone are already lonely if they have nothing of any greater value to fill their lives.

The way to overcome fear of loneliness is to begin – now – to build a safety net of people you care about and things you enjoy doing. Then, even if one person or thing is unavailable, there will be plenty left to support you.

Ultimately we may build many bridges to connect us to the people and things we love, but we all have to take responsibility for ourselves. Those who wait for someone else to come along and take away all their loneliness and fear are likely to wait forever.

FEAR OF FOOD

Food is not the enemy. The slice of cake lying on your plate is not going to jump up and grab you by the throat, the bag of greasy chips is not going to hurl abuse at you in the street. It is your attitude towards food that is wrong. It is your lack of control where food and eating is concerned that causes you to be afraid.

If you have reached the stage where you find it impossible to eat a potato because you are terrified that you will get fat, you have a very real problem. It is probably safe to assume that if something as simple as potatoes can inspire so much fear, then the rest of your life is fear-ridden as well.

The way back is to take it a step at a time. Eat a small potato, be aware of your terror and how you are facing it and overcoming it as you eat. Next day you will discover that you have not put on weight from that potato and therefore it is not your enemy, you no longer need to fear it. This is your first battle won, from here you can go on to face all your other fears.

DO IT

Whatever your particular fear, however it grips you, to overcome it you have to take action. Do something positive to face up to your fear and already it begins to lose its power. Fear does not exist except in the mind of the fearful person.

13 Depression

Just when you begin to think you are really making some progress in sorting out your eating and your life – sticking to the Eating Plan and taking stock of your emotional problems – along comes one more setback: depression.

It is extremely common for people with eating disorders to get dragged down by depression, not only when in the depths of their compulsion but on the way out. It is a pitfall everyone has to watch out for and be prepared to cope with or it could undo all the good work done so far.

ARE YOU DEPRESSED?

It may not have occurred to you that you are depressed. You may have lived with a poor quality of life for so long that you have forgotten what it is like to feel light-hearted and on top of the world. Or perhaps some tragic event has overwhelmed you and so you put your feelings of misery down to grief rather than thinking of them as depression. Try to analyse your state of mind by considering the questions overleaf:

There is little point in taking anti-depressants for months or even years just because your doctor prescribes them – indeed, most doctors no longer agree that depressed patients should be treated in this way. When you are stuck in the depressive rut, however, a course of anti-depressants can be useful in breaking the cycle of despair and giving you a breathing space to tackle the things causing your depression. If your doctor does prescribe them for you, use the time when you are on them wisely to make changes, so that next time you visit the doctor you will no longer need them. You may find at first that you suffer some side-effects from taking the anti-depressants, such as drowsiness or a dry mouth. Don't let this put you off and do not be afraid that you will become addicted to them.

Table 17 ARE YOU DEPRESSED?

	Never	Sometimes	Often	Always
1. Do you feel overwhelmed by total despair?	☐	☐	☐	☐
2. Do you feel a failure?	☐	☐	☐	☐
3. Do you feel helpless about your life and situation?	☐	☐	☐	☐
4. Do you have trouble concentrating?	☐	☐	☐	☐
5. Do you find it difficult to make decisions?	☐	☐	☐	☐
6. Do you get suicidal thoughts?	☐	☐	☐	☐
7. Do you lack interest in:				
a) work	☐	☐	☐	☐
b) friends	☐	☐	☐	☐
c) hobbies	☐	☐	☐	☐
d) life in general	☐	☐	☐	☐
8. Do you feel it is not worth bothering about:				
a) making and keeping friends	☐	☐	☐	☐
b) doing a good job at work	☐	☐	☐	☐
c) trying to improve the quality of your life	☐	☐	☐	☐
d) getting your eating under control	☐	☐	☐	☐
e) sorting out your problems	☐	☐	☐	☐
f) your appearance	☐	☐	☐	☐
g) anything at all	☐	☐	☐	☐
9. Do you suffer from:				
a) extreme lethargy	☐	☐	☐	☐
b) restlessness	☐	☐	☐	☐
c) poor sleep	☐	☐	☐	☐
d) chronic tiredness	☐	☐	☐	☐
e) headaches	☐	☐	☐	☐
f) tearfulness	☐	☐	☐	☐

SCORING

If you answered Often or Always to most of these questions you are likely to be suffering from depression. If you have not already discussed this with your doctor it is advisable that you do so straight away. These days the medical answer is not always an immediate and lengthy prescription for anti-depressants, although it may be helpful to take this form of medication for a while.

Note: Your score may alter depending on your mood on a particular day or at a particular time. It's worth filling in this questionnaire more than once, at different times of day, to begin to understand your individual mood patterns.

Although it is commonly believed that anti-depressants are addictive, this is not true – this myth has come about by people confusing them with tranquillizers, which are highly addictive and should only be used with great caution.

If you still don't feel able to tackle life after a short time on anti-depressants, ask your doctor to recommend you seek further treatment such as seeing a therapist rather than just accepting a further course of anti-depressants. At the same time you must make a huge effort to help yourself – you will never beat your depression (or your eating problem) if you sit back and wait for someone else to do the work for you.

There are several different types of depression. It is a vast subject covering many symptoms and degrees of suffering. In extreme cases, such as manic depression or where there are suicidal feelings, it is important to receive professional help. Research seems to indicate that out of the millions of people who suffer from depression most feel too ashamed to seek help.

WHAT STARTED IT?

First try and work out what brought your depression on. It is quite common to suffer from depression after a physical illness. Viral illnesses, anything from flu to hepatitis, deplete the body and upset its natural chemical balances. Extra rest and good nutrition are particularly important after an illness. You may need professional advice about vitamin and mineral supplements. Alternative therapies such as acupuncture and homoeopathy can be particularly useful here, with supplemental treatments such as shiatsu or aromatherapy to help clear a build-up of toxins in your body and leave you pleasantly relaxed.

A life-threatening illness can frequently be followed by a bout of depression, as anything that brings a person face-to-face with his own mortality can stir up some very deep-rooted emotions. Don't be afraid to talk about how you are feeling, but make sure you pick the right person to talk to. If you don't know anyone sympathetic and emotionally stable to lean on at such a time, go to see a counsellor – again your doctor should be able to refer you. Self-help groups can also be very supportive and there is sure to be one in your area. Once you overcome the hurdle of going for the first time you may well find getting to know others with similar problems very helpful.

HORMONAL CAUSES

Post-natal depression is very common in the days after childbirth when hormone levels are in turmoil and your body has a lot of adjustments to make. Hormonal changes can also trigger depression at the time of the menopause, often coupled with emotional distress at coming to terms with no longer being fertile. Don't delay in seeking medical help, hormone replacement therapy may be the answer.

Hormone treatment may also be called for in severe cases of premenstrual tension. PMT can lead to depression, among other things. If your PMT is not this critical but still gives you a bad time every month there are various things you can do to help yourself:

- Try to plan your life to avoid stressful activities at this time.
- Take extra rest. At the same time, don't neglect exercise as it will lift you both physically and emotionally.
- Take extra care with your diet, in particular avoiding high-carbohydrate foods, but realize that your body will actually need extra calories before a period and allow yourself to eat more. Blood sugar levels tend to drop more quickly at this time – hence increased cravings for sweets.
- Some people find that taking Vitamin B$_6$ and Oil of Evening Primrose helps to ease premenstrual symptoms. The Women's

Nutritional Advisory Service recommend a mineral and vitamin supplement called *Optivite* which is particularly high in chromium and magnesium, the two minerals that help to stabilize blood sugar levels. This supplement is available through the Maisner Centre.

REACTIVE CAUSES

Reactive depression is usually easy to account for. It occurs as a direct result of some very stressful event, in particular the death of someone close, the break-up of a close relationship or the loss of home, job or business. It is natural to need time to mourn a bereavement or loss. Do not be too hard on yourself if you feel utterly miserable to begin with. Specialized bereavement counselling can be very helpful and supportive when you are trying to come to terms with the loss of someone close to you. After a while you will come to realize that life goes on and that somehow you have to pick yourself up and start again. It is at this point that taking a short course of anti-depressants may well help you to turn the corner and begin living again.

THE OTHER SORT

The most difficult form of depression to come to terms with is the kind that seems to hit you out of the blue for no apparent reason. You have to be prepared to be honest with yourself and look a bit closer at your life to find the hidden cause of this kind of depression.

For example, if you have an eating disorder and have been starving and bingeing for any length of time, particularly if you are also bulimic, your body chemistry will be disturbed and you are likely to be suffering from huge swings in blood sugar levels. This alone is enough to bring on depression, but the fact that you have an eating problem in the first place probably points to other disturbances in your life that need sorting out.

Following the Eating Plan should do a lot towards making you feel physically more stable and may be enough on its own to lift you out of the depression. Actually starting to face up to your problems and trying to make changes can, unfortunately, bring on depression at first, before you work through the blocks and really get back in full control of your life. Even little things may begin to annoy you. While you were so wrapped up in thoughts of eating, food and weight you may not have noticed that your youngest son sniffs continually, your husband sings loudly in the bathroom and the car door rattles. Suddenly these things start to invade your conscious mind and drive you mad. Think positively, this is an excellent sign. It means you are coming out of your trap and beginning to live in the world again.

If you have been shutting your eyes to things that are very wrong, pushing them out of sight and mind and suppressing difficult emotions by eating, you may well feel overwhelmed by despair when you finally find the courage to take a good look around again.

Recognize that this might happen. Look on it as proof that you are working in a positive way towards improving your life. Remain determined to work through the bad times. You are coming close to those things that are actually causing your eating problem - until you sort them out once and for all you will never get your eating under control.

FACING THE MONSTER

It may help to picture your problems in terms of ancient legend. The people are terrorized by a monster. Only when the hero comes along and fights and kills the monster can the people live happily again. All the time you allow your personal monster to go on living (whether it is made up of a bad relationship, haunting memories of the past, lack of self-worth) you will exist in its shadow. You have to be your own St George and tackle and overcome the monster within you, then you will find you no longer need to binge.

Tackling this on your own is very difficult. When a person is depressed she lacks the very motivation she needs so desperately to drag herself out of her miserable rut. Frequent doses of inspiration and motivation are usually required - you have to make sure you put yourself in situations where you can receive them. There are plenty of workshops and seminars based on improving self-esteem, self-assertiveness and communication. Although you may find it very difficult to take part in something like this at first, the positive atmosphere generated by such events is very supportive. Your local health food shop, natural health centre, new age shop, adult education centre, library or Citizens Advice Bureau is likely to have details of such workshops and the people who run them.

To give you a little extra inspiration along the way, here is a piece by someone who suffered seriously from bulimia and managed to turn back. She wrote this on her way back to recovery:

> I have a picture on my lounge wall of two dolphins swimming. Above them the sun is emerging from the clouds. Today is the first day I have ever noticed that sun, and it feels like *my* sun. Even though the day outside is dull, inside I feel my abilities and character breaking through the clouds of suppression that I had imposed on myself in the form of food.
>
> My mind no longer has that fog - I can plan better, think more clearly and tackle my problems more efficiently. I am learning to have faith in myself again.

Sounds dramatic? - You try sitting around under a dark cloud for 14 years!

HOW IT FEELS

Most people suffer from some form of depression at some time in their lives. For some it is just a passing phase, others suffer terribly until they come out the other side very different people. Still others drag along in misery year after year permanently wrapped in despair, spreading a grey blanket of gloom wherever they go.

How often do thoughts go round and round in your head in a way similar to those shown in Figure 8?

Depression is very self-defeating. Whereas it may be possible to find the courage and hope to fight against a physical illness, depression robs its victims of the capacity to fight back. They are left to battle it out handicapped and unarmed. The greatest handicap is the overwhelming feeling that nothing is worth bothering about, there is no light to be seen anywhere and every effort to shake off the depression appears utterly futile.

This is particularly true if depression has come on or is intensified as a result of trying to get to grips with deep-rooted problems and compulsive behaviour.

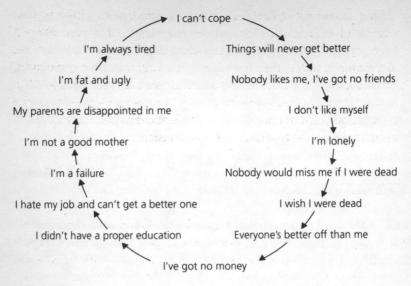

I can't cope

I'm always tired

Things will never get better

I'm fat and ugly

Nobody likes me, I've got no friends

My parents are disappointed in me

I don't like myself

I'm not a good mother

I'm lonely

I'm a failure

Nobody would miss me if I were dead

I hate my job and can't get a better one

I wish I were dead

I didn't have a proper education

Everyone's better off than me

I've got no money

Figure 8

Mike is a typical example of this. He had become an alcoholic and had also developed eating problems. His drab life revolved around eating and drinking. When he decided to make a real effort to give up drinking he was successful at first, kicking the alcohol and greatly improving his eating habits. It seemed he was well on the road to changing his life radically for the better.

However, after a couple of months instead of feelings of lightness and release he was hit by a bad bout of depression. He hovered on the brink of returning to his old lifestyle. Everywhere he looked he saw things that annoyed and depressed him further. His flatmate Andy was an alcoholic. They had been good mates when they both shared the addiction, but now Mike could not bear to be in the same room with him. They argued all the time, making the atmosphere in the flat terrible. At work things were no better because Mike worked in a pub which suddenly seemed to be packed with people addicted to alcohol – something he had never noticed before. All of a sudden he felt isolated. He no longer had anything in common with the people in his life and he asked himself seriously whether it was all worth while. He felt he had lost more than he had gained by trying to get to grips with his drinking and eating problems.

Mike was starting to slip back into his old binge/diet pattern when he met Kathy. She was the first person he had known in a long time who did not have an eating or drink problem. She introduced him to a whole new set of acquaintances with values and interests that were different from anything he had encountered before. One day he went for a picnic in the country with Kathy and her young sons. Sitting on the green grass, breathing fresh air and watching the children playing happily, Mike realized there was a whole world that he had lost touch with. It was the turning point that motivated him to make real changes in his life. From then on he was able to shake off his depression.

TAKING RISKS

Mike was taking a risk when he gave up drinking and bingeing. He was taking a risk when he stepped outside the world that was familiar and became involved with Kathy. If he had not taken these risks he would still be caught up in his old life. It is only by risk-taking that you discover what exists outside your own front door. It is safer to stay indoors, but you will never achieve anything really worthwhile nor ever find fulfilment while you only wish you could step outside but never dare take the risk. Try thinking of it as a long journey. If it seems too daunting to contemplate the whole distance, just plan to go one step at a time. When you have arrived successfully at your first destination you can consider how you are going to tackle the next leg of the journey.

HIDDEN STRENGTH

Many people with eating problems who are caught up in depression discover a strength and survival instinct in themselves they had lost touch with all the time they were clinging to their old self-destructive ways. It is not until they commit themselves to taking risks and making changes that they discover a whole new person living inside the old. You may not think you have sufficient courage to take risks, but if you go out and take them with faith the necessary courage will come.

Lack of self-esteem makes it easy to underestimate what we are capable of. If we never put ourselves to the test we will never discover what we can do. Nowhere is this more true than when faced with tackling an eating disorder.

SELF-HELP

There are plenty of things you can do for yourself to escape from depression, if you are prepared to take the risk. For example:

- Make sure you get enough rest, relaxation and sleep. If you are permanently tired, tense and on edge you will not be ready to take advantage of opportunities that come along.
- Take up an interesting hobby, preferably something that gets you out and meeting other people. A passion for collecting stamps is better than having no interests at all, but a solitary pursuit is not ideal if you want to overcome the isolation that is often linked with depression.
- Get out of the house for at least part of every day. Sitting alone at home will only feed your despair and encourage you to binge. If you haven't an occupation consider ways in which you could get one – or try college or even doing voluntary work to help those worse off than yourself. Be prepared to take the risk of sending off job applications and of asking others what you can do to help them.
- Join a self-help group for people suffering from depression so you can work on your problems together. A lot of towns have day centres. If not, take a chance and put an advertisement in your local paper, along the lines:
  'Depressed bulimic seeks others to form mutual self-help group.' Give a box number so you are in control of the replies you get. It is unlikely you will receive anything but a positive response.
- Take plenty of exercise. Swimming and walking are very beneficial in many ways, while joining an exercise class or sports club will also be a way of meeting new people. How about dog-walking – your own or someone else's? It gets you out and you will find that people smile and chat to you when you are with a dog.
- Don't dwell on the past. It is very easy to slip into familiar thought patterns about how things have gone wrong in the past; your brain goes round and round the same old track, getting nowhere. You have to learn to be very strict with yourself: every time you catch these thoughts slipping into your head, just say firmly, 'No. I am not going to think about that now. I am going to think about something positive instead.' In a surprisingly short time you will find you are breaking the negative-thought habit.

However, in breaking this 'hamster in a wheel' syndrome do not fall into the trap of suppressing your problems. If there is something that is really bothering you it needs to be talked through with a professional counsellor. Discuss your problem and be open to ways of solving it. You may have a sympathetic and supportive friend or family member you can talk to, but try to realize that nobody is going to go on listening to you moaning endlessly about your problems if you show no positive signs of making changes to solve them.

Penny and Kim had been best friends at school and still kept in touch regularly, taking it in turns to phone each other every week. Because Kim was a good listener, when Penny's life started going downhill she found herself listening for hours to all of Penny's problems. Week after week it was the same thing. Then one week Kim didn't phone; another week went by and still no call. After three weeks Penny rang her and asked why she hadn't heard from her. 'Quite honestly Penny, I'm bored with listening to you moaning on about the same old things every week,' Kim replied. 'When you can tell me you are going to do something about your problems I'll be pleased to help you.' Penny was shocked at first to hear her sympathetic friend talk to her like this, but she had known Kim long enough to realize Kim was only saying this to help her. She realized she had to try and do something about solving her problems instead of endlessly complaining while doing nothing.

LOOKING GOOD

Take an interest in your appearance. When people get depressed they tend to ignore how they dress and how they look. One tell-tale sign of a bulimic is that she often dresses in black because she thinks it makes her look slimmer. Try wearing bright colours, it is surprising what a difference it makes to your mood if you change your black jumper for a red one. Get out in the sunshine, put a brighter bulb in your lamp, have fresh flowers in your bedroom - generally surround yourself with more brightness and colour to lift your spirits. Get your hair cut in a new style, or have a full manicure and pedicure. Treat yourself. Lack of money is no excuse - hairdressers and beauty schools are always pleased to have models to work on and there is rarely more than a nominal charge.

Stand up straight and take a look around. It is easy to walk around with your eyes on the ground and your shoulders slumped. Have you noticed the blossoms on the tree, the sea at the end of the road, the piles of fresh ripe fruit on the greengrocer's stall? When you are miserable the world seems a gloomy place, when you feel cheerful other people seem to be smiling and everything seems brighter.

Make a note of your successes, however small. Write them down in a special notebook so you can refer to them frequently. It is easy to forget the positive things and dwell too much on the negative, so make a chart to show your progress and pin it up on the wall so you see it every day.

Make the decision to develop a positive attitude towards everything you do, think and say, from now on.

14 Stress

A certain amount of stress is a good thing. It perks up the system and keeps us on our toes. If life were all bland and stress-free we would soon become lethargic and bored. It is only when stress becomes 'distress' that problems begin – and the exact point where one becomes the other is unique to every individual.

You cannot judge how much stress you should be able to cope with by other people's standards – or what you perceive other people's standards to be. If your colleagues at work seem able to work longer and harder than you without distress that doesn't mean you are a failure if you get tired, lose concentration or suffer headaches when your job puts you under pressure. Learn how much you can cope with *before* you feel stressed and then:

- Arrange your life to suit your personal boundaries.
- Work on raising your levels of emotional and physical fitness to enable you to expand those boundaries with ease.
- Find a positive alternative to bingeing when you overstep your stress boundaries.

ARE YOU UNDER STRESS?

Most of the common symptoms of stress can also be caused by a number of other conditions such as depression or physical illness. If you can eliminate other reasons yet you still suffer from a combination of some of the following physical and emotional symptoms, and you are living under conditions that you find less than ideal, it is likely that stress is your problem.

SOME PHYSICAL SIGNS OF STRESS

How many of the following affect you, either on a daily basis or from time to time when you are under particular pressure? Almost all of these can also be signs of depression, and stress can lead to depression if it is not recognized and dealt with.

- Disturbed sleep patterns: difficulty getting to sleep, frequent waking in the night, waking early and being unable to get back to sleep
- Sexual difficulties: impotence, lack of desire for sex, need for excessive sex
- Restlessness: inability to sit still, nervous habits such as touching your face, pulling at your clothes
- Physical discomforts: frequent headaches, heartburn, queasiness, high blood-pressure, dizzy spells, breathlessness, tightness in the chest, sweating for no obvious reason
- Erratic bowel function: constipation or diarrhoea
- Disturbances in appetite: strong desire to eat outside meal times, loss of appetite at meal times, bingeing
- Crying easily or feeling the desire to cry
- Needing a drink to 'unwind'
- Smoking to calm your nerves

SOME EMOTIONAL SIGNS OF STRESS

- Lack of interest in life
- Irritability for no obvious reason
- Irrational fears: of disease, accidents, thieves and muggers, open spaces, enclosed spaces, failure, of the future, of crowds, of being alone
- Difficulty making decisions
- Difficulty concentrating on one thing, or in finishing one job before rushing on to the next
- Difficulty relaxing and being able to laugh
- Inability to let go of an idea, a relationship, a situation

For compulsive eaters the list of things likely to cause stress is expanded by additional fears and worries such as:

- fear of getting fat(ter)
- fear of bingeing

- fear of vomiting
- fear of being caught or seen bingeing or vomiting
- fear of somebody knowing you have got a problem
- fear that somebody who knows about your problem will tell someone else
- fear of damaging your body through bingeing or vomiting
- fear of not being able to be sick when the occasion arises
- fear of not being able to binge when the occasion arises
- guilt about spending too much money on food

ANXIETY TENDENCY CHECKLIST

The chart in Table 18 was designed by Dr Charles Spielberger, Professor of Psychology at the University of South Florida, as a means of evaluating an individual's tendency towards anxiety. Anxiety is a major feature of both stress and depression.

Read each statement and then circle the appropriate number that indicates how you generally feel. There are no right or wrong answers. Do not spend too much time on any one statement, but give the answer that seems to describe how you generally feel. Add up the eight numbers you have circled to obtain your score.

Table 18

	Almost Never	Sometimes	Often	Almost Always
I feel nervous and restless	1	2	3	4
I feel satisfied with myself	4	3	2	1
I feel that difficulties are piling up so that I cannot overcome them	1	2	3	4
I feel a failure	1	2	3	4
I have violent thoughts of hurting myself or others	1	2	3	4
I lack self-confidence	1	2	3	4
I feel secure	4	3	2	1
I worry too much over things that really do not matter	1	2	3	4

Only five per cent of the population has a score of ten or less. Half the population has a score of around 15, only five per cent of the population has a score of over 20. If you have scored over 15 you are too stressed and should do something about it.

HOW TO BEAT STRESS

The way to beat stress is to remove the thing or things that are causing it. It may not be possible to eradicate the cause completely, but you should aim to reduce it to manageable proportions. For example, if driving in traffic brings on serious stress you should consider 1) changing your job if it involves a lot of driving, 2) travelling more by public transport or 3) moving to a quieter part of the country. All of these are big decisions, involving major life changes, but sometimes drastic situations call for drastic measures. If you have a heart attack at the wheel one day you will be forced to make big changes, so consider the options *now* while you still have free choice.

There are plenty of other ways to cut down on your stress load. Read the checklist (Table 19) and see how many of the following you are using to help yourself live a more stress-free life:

Table 19

	Yes	Sometimes	No
Do you limit your working week to 5½ days if you work away from home?	☐	☐	☐
If you work at home, do you build in time for leisure?	☐	☐	☐
Do you limit your working day to 10 hours or less?	☐	☐	☐
Do you find time to take at least ½ hour over each main meal?	☐	☐	☐
Do you eat slowly and enjoy your food?	☐	☐	☐
Do you get at least seven hours sleep a night?	☐	☐	☐
Do you spend time listening to relaxing music?	☐	☐	☐
Do you practise relaxation or meditation daily?	☐	☐	☐

Do you play sport or attend exercise sessions at least three times a week? ☐ ☐ ☐

Do you have a hobby or creative outlet? ☐ ☐ ☐

Do you have a regular break from your children? ☐ ☐ ☐

Do you have regular massage, beauty treatment or something to make you feel good? ☐ ☐ ☐

Do you spend at least ½ hour daily out of doors? ☐ ☐ ☐

Do you have an annual holiday away from your usual environment? ☐ ☐ ☐

Ideally you should have answered 'Yes' to every question. Try paying more attention to the points for which you answered 'No.' Take this test again in six months to see whether you are looking after yourself better.

Having looked at things you can do to ease your stress load, there are further things you *don't* need to do when stressed, such as:

- Don't feel embarrassed about seeking professional help with any emotional or sexual problem that is causing distress.
- Don't overspend, get into debt or commit yourself to more than you can afford. If you get into financial trouble seek help at once from your bank, building society or the Citizens Advice Bureau.
- Don't take on more work and responsibilities than you can cope with comfortably. Avoid over-committing yourself to others. Allow yourself your own personal time and space.
- Don't worry about your health. See your doctor if you have a problem and talk to him or her honestly about all your symptoms and how you are feeling.
- Don't worry about what other people may be thinking of you. Your worries are probably groundless, they are more likely to be worrying about what you are thinking of them.
- Exercise regularly (at least two or three times a week). Choose a form of exercise suited to your health and personal fitness level. Being 'always on the go' or running around after the children all day is not the same as exercise and will not produce the same benefits.
- Learn to relax. Yoga combines relaxation and meditation with exercise, while relaxation tapes are useful to play at home. For help with eating problems the Maisner Centre can supply a

special tape that includes relaxation techniques. The Alexander Technique teaches posture and body awareness.

- Cut out caffeine and avoid turning to alcohol as an anti-stress measure.
- Get enough sleep.
- Laugh and enjoy life. Watch funny films, read amusing books, spend time with people who have a good sense of humour. Do something that really absorbs you and takes your mind off everything else.

MAKE IT HAPPEN

By now you may realize that you are under a greater stress load than you can cope with. Hopefully you feel you would like to do something about reducing it. It is, however, very easy to discover excuses for carrying on in the same stressful lifestyle.

Laurel is a good example of this. She works for the government, arriving at her desk at 7.30 each morning and never leaving before 6 in the evening, often without taking a proper break the entire day. She got into this habit of working long hours when she was hoping for promotion some years ago, now if questioned she says she has a huge workload and the department would not run smoothly if she slowed down.

Privately Laurel has other reasons she does not like to admit even to herself. She lives alone in a small flat, has few friends, no outside interests and suffers greatly from loneliness when she is not at the office. She has an eating problem that has gradually got worse over the years. She is afraid that when she is alone at home she will binge. Even lunchtimes can be a danger and on many occasions she avoids taking a lunch break to prevent herself from going out and overeating. She has got into the familiar circle where stress exacerbates her eating problem and her eating problem increases her stress load. She needs to make some drastic life changes before stress brings her to breaking point.

CONQUERING LONELINESS

Loneliness is a great cause of stress and depression. Although many busy people - particularly mothers with demanding families - often crave time to themselves, too much of a good thing can be as stressful as none at all. Loneliness can be very much a state of mind. It is possible to be perfectly content on one's own or very lonely in a large crowd.

You make the choice about how lonely you wish to be. There is never any real reason to be lonely, unless you are shipwrecked on a desert island or locked in solitary confinement. Over-population is one of the world's worst problems, there is no lack of people to get to know. The problem is knowing how to make the right relationships.

There is little point going around with a crowd of people you don't like just for the sake of not being lonely. Making new friends also involves areas of risk. If you offer friendship you risk being rejected, if you feel love for another you risk being hurt – but if you never take these risks you will always be lonely. Consider the following questions about yourself and your current relationships:

1. Do you consider yourself lonely?
2. Do you spend time doing things you don't want to do or with people you don't like, just to avoid being alone?
3. Do you want to be alone so that you can binge?
4. Do you dread being alone because you are afraid you will binge?
5. Is there any person or persons you feel really close to, or do all your relationships seem superficial?
6. Is there somebody you would like to get to know better but are afraid of taking the initiative?
7. Do you feel you have something to offer as a friend?
8. Do you feel you are so wrapped up in yourself that you have nothing to give to others?
9. Do you feel you give too much of yourself, your time and your attention to your friends?
10. Are you happy to listen to what others have to say?
11. Do you feel others pay attention to you when you are speaking?

Friendship is very much a two-way street. There is no point in offering your time and effort endlessly to someone who does not appreciate you. At the same time you cannot expect others to be your friends if you have nothing to give back. If you are wrapped up in yourself, your own world and your problems – particularly if your life is dominated by your eating so nothing else seems to matter - it is hardly surprising that others do not go out of their way to try and penetrate your thick armour.

DEVELOPING SOCIAL SKILLS

Shyness causes many people to be lonely. Many people did not learn any social skills when they were young, perhaps because their childhood was isolated or disturbed, or because their parents lacked these skills and were unable to teach them. They have entered adult life unprepared to handle friendships and relationships; maybe they tried to get to know people and made mistakes or were rejected so they've given up trying and have resigned themselves to a lonely life.

Social skills such as how to make friends, have good relationships with people, how to talk to strangers and feel confident at parties and in mixed company are all things that can be learned. There are books you can buy, or borrow from the library - or better still classes and workshops where you are likely to meet people with similar problems. A public speaking course can increase self-confidence immensely, particularly if you feel your career is being held back because of your shyness.

You may be interested in exploring the possibilities of co-counselling. This is a two-way process of mutual aid, in which two people take it in turns to work on any issue that concerns them. First you need to attend a course to learn the basic skills, which will give you access to the Co-counselling International Network. The idea is that you work in pairs, calling on a fellow co-counsellor when you have a particular problem to sort out. At the same time you help him or her with a problem. You do not necessarily work with the same person all the time. This method is used by many people to help them with their own development and to get support in dealing with life and work problems.

LET OTHERS HELP

There are many caring and well-meaning people around who can give you help and support while you are working on the difficult task of getting your eating under control. Help from others will make the job a lot easier, but others cannot help you unless:

1. You tell them that you have a problem and ask for help.
2. You are prepared to do the hard work yourself, relying on others purely for moral support and encouragement. Nobody can do the job for you.
3. You do not overwhelm them with your problems, complaining endlessly about your difficulties and talking continually about how hard done by you are.
4. You become aware that your friends have their own problems and are prepared to spend time listening to and supporting them as well.

The best way to have a friend is to be a friend. If someone is important to you make sure you treat her with consideration, complimenting her on her achievements, thanking her for the things she does for you, being aware of those times she is feeling low and giving her special attention even if it means sacrificing something you want to do. The best way to avoid loneliness is genuinely to enjoy the company of other people, then you will find plenty of people all around you who are more than willing to enjoy your company.

Commitment is a word that horrifies most compulsive eaters. They feel so out of control of their own lives they dread being expected to fit in with other people's arrangements. However, anyone who wants to become part of a social group has to make some sort of commitment to the other members or they will soon get exasperated.

If you join a class or course of workshops, pay in advance so that you make a financial commitment. If you know holidays and weekends are your bad times for bingeing make plans in advance that involve committing yourself to a place or a person at these times. If you receive an invitation accept it at once. When the time comes be there – never allow yourself to think up an excuse not to go.

A WOMAN'S PLACE

Lack of self-esteem is at the root of another great source of stress: trying always to be perfect. Too many women feel they have to keep their house spotlessly clean, be model mothers, ideal wives or girlfriends and perhaps hard-working wage-earners as well. They never allow themselves to fail, or even not to triumph. Keeping up such a model of perfection is extremely stressful.

It would be a generalization to say that life is always more stressful for women than it is for men. The two sexes have different sorts of pressures to cope with, but women are often exposed to stresses that men generally don't have to cope with.

For example, when Mrs Thatcher became Prime Minister the press began to comment on her appearance and the way she dressed in a way that no male politician had ever had to cope with. She was quite assertive enough to nip that sort of reporting in the bud, but other women who shoot suddenly into the limelight have found this media attention on their appearance disastrously stressful.

Traditionally men can come home from work and slump in front of the television, while women are expected to do the cooking and cleaning after a full day's work at the office. If the children are ill it is usually mother who is expected to take time off work to look after them.

Women themselves must take a lot of the responsibility for this situation. Many are too willing to accept the role of general dogsbody, just as men are willing to take advantage of this. Women can and should learn to be assertive and improve the quality of their lives - without turning into overbearing monsters. A woman is a person with rights who is worthy of respect. She does not need to put herself down or in the role of servant unless she chooses to do so through a lack of self-esteem.

Training in assertiveness and self-esteem can improve radically not only how a woman sees herself and her role in life but also how others perceive her. An assertive person tends to be treated with greater respect by others because they sense she has a feeling of her own worth. She can care for her family, do a useful day's work and run her home efficiently yet be happy with her life because she is doing what she chooses to do, not struggling under the stressful burden of feeling she is not worth anything better. See page 215 for further details of where to go for assertiveness training.

Each of the different stages of motherhood - caring for the crying baby or wayward teenager, living with an empty nest - carries its own kind of stress. Each is also quite able to drive a woman to the comfort of food and the security of eating. But bingeing is never the answer.

STRESS AT WORK

The stress that arises at home can sometimes be exacerbated by stress at work. Sticking at a job you hate because you think you can't manage without the money is one reason for stress of this kind. If the stress is making you binge, however, try working out just how much of your hard-earned cash is wasted on binge foods.

Consider the following questions and decide whether your job is stimulating your life or is a dead weight, dragging you down.

Table 20 SHOULD I STAY IN MY JOB?

	Yes	No
1. Is fear of what lies ahead preventing me from making the decision to leave?	☐	☐
2. Am I staying in my job mainly because I have invested a lot of time in training for it?	☐	☐
3. Will my physical health be threatened if I stay in this job?	☐	☐
4. Am I staying in this job even though I have more to gain by leaving?	☐	☐
5. Will my mental health be affected if I stay in this job?	☐	☐
6. Am I experiencing a lack of personal fulfilment in my work?	☐	☐
7. Am I staying because of economic security?	☐	☐
8. Am I staying because I am frightened of change?	☐	☐
9. Am I exhausted at the end of every working day?	☐	☐
10. Will my superiors be upset if I leave?	☐	☐
11. Am I remaining because I don't want to cause other people disruption?	☐	☐
12. Do I enjoy being with my colleagues?	☐	☐
13. Do I receive encouragement and support from my superiors?	☐	☐
14. Do I experience more criticism than praise?	☐	☐
15. Do I like my job?	☐	☐

SCORING

1. Yes	2	No	0
2. Yes	2	No	0

3. Yes	4	No	0
4. Yes	2	No	0
5. Yes	4	No	0
6. Yes	3	No	0
7. Yes	3	No	0
8. Yes	3	No	0
9. Yes	3	No	0
10. Yes	4	No	0
11. Yes	3	No	0
12. Yes	0	No	2
13. Yes	0	No	3
14. Yes	3	No	0
15. Yes	0	No	4

Less than 10. You are fortunate to have a job that is a positive part of your life.

11–20. Make sure you have a fulfilling life away from work to compensate for the few drawbacks you find in your work.

Over 21. Your job is not satisfactory and is a negative influence on your life. You should be looking towards making changes, either by giving up work and finding a new job, or perhaps altering radically the attitude you have towards the job at present.

DOES YOUR WORK MAKE YOU FAT?

There are certain professions well known for creating eating problems. Perhaps the best-known are modelling, dancing and being a professional jockey. People in these professions need to be excessively slim and lightweight to succeed. They know that putting on weight would mean losing their job and this adds extra stress to an already demanding lifestyle.

Plenty of other jobs have built-in factors that may affect a person's eating habits, such as:

● The nurse who works unsociable hours that throw her body clock out of rhythm.

Those who go into the caring professions tend to place great importance on pleasing others and disregard the needs of their own bodies and emotions. They give and give and feel guilty if they need help with a problem themselves.

- The business executive who is expected to entertain lavishly and easily gets caught up in a world of drinking too much and eating rich foods.

Working breakfasts, business lunches and formal dinners are the norm – and the ambitious executive may be afraid she will seem rude or disinterested if she turns an invitation down.

- The opera singer who cannot eat for several hours before a performance and tends to overeat afterwards to compensate for natural hunger, emotional strain and very low blood sugar levels.

CONSIDER YOUR WORK

Look at the following three statements. If your job is a positive force in your life you should be able to answer Yes to points 1 and 2 and No to 3. If you have any doubts about being able to answer in this way, your working life needs close attention if you want to succeed in getting your eating permanently under control.

1. Do you enjoy your job?

This lies at the root of whether you are under too much stress at work or not. If you are happy and fulfilled most of the time in what you do you will be able to ride out the stressful times successfully.

2. Does your job allow you to eat sensible, regular meals?

It is a legal requirement that employers allow their employees suitable breaks. If pressure is being put on you not to take a break, you need to be more assertive. Find out exactly what you are entitled to and ensure you are not taken advantage of. Realistic meal and drink breaks are not only your right but ultimately of benefit to your employer – you will work better if your body and brain are sensibly nourished.

If your ban on breaks is self-imposed you need to look at your own standards more closely and consider your own needs. If you are self-employed, work from home and/or are your own boss it is easy to slip into undisciplined habits such as working for long stretches and then overeating out of stress, tiredness and low blood sugar.

If the office canteen only offers cakes and sweets, bring your own healthy snacks, or suggest to the catering manager some sensible alternatives – that way you'll be helping your co-workers as well.

3. Does your job put you under more pressure than you can handle?

Again, look at whether your employer is being unreasonable or whether you are choosing to take on too heavy a load. In the long run nobody wins if one person cracks under the strain of trying to do too much. Learning to pace yourself is a discipline that helps not only at work but in all aspects of life, especially with regard to eating.

SEXUAL PROBLEMS

Almost every marriage or relationship will run into sexual problems at some time. Physical changes, illness and stressful life situations can all be reflected in a lack of sexual harmony between two people. It is up to both partners to work through the difficult times if they want their relationship to succeed.

When one partner has a compulsive problem such as abusing alcohol, drugs or food this inevitably puts stress on the relationship. If a woman is a compulsive eater she will go to great lengths to avoid sexual advances when she is feeling fat, bloated and ugly or when she is suffering from the after-effects of a binge.

The other partner seldom understands fully the compulsive partner's conflict and turmoil. He only knows he is being rejected, that his partner is always miserable and depressed and too wrapped up in herself to give him the attention he needs. He either continues to live a miserable life or seeks out someone else to give him the attention he is missing at home.

This is just one aspect of the ways in which difficult relationships can exaggerate and eating problem or an eating problem can lead to relationship problems, as the next chapter explores in more detail.

15 Relationships

Although compulsive eating and particularly bulimia are invariably isolated habits indulged in in secret, the knock-on effects of uncontrolled eating can make a dramatic difference to any relationship in which the compulsive eater is involved.

CHILDHOOD

The first important relationship we have in our lives is with our parents. It is here that so many problems are born and carry on haunting us long after we have grown into adulthood.

Many people look back and see that their problems with food started in childhood or adolescence, where adverse relationships with parents were a major influence. Most parents want the best for their children but often they do not truly understand that their children are individuals. They try to impose their own standards, often with disastrous results.

Juliet is one example of how this works. Her mother always impressed on her the importance of looking smart and having a good figure. Although her mother was naturally slim, Juliet took after her father who had a tendency to put weight on easily. Her mother never wearied in the endless struggle against Juliet's 'puppy fat', endlessly repeating such phrases as 'People will think better of you if you look nice and slim' and 'Boys don't want to go out with fat girls.' She was proud of the lovely teenager she had raised and was totally unable to relate to the thin, unhealthy girl Juliet turned into when she went to university and became bulimic.

Away from home for the first time, Juliet had to face up to a lot of new pressures. She responded to these pressures in accordance with her mother's training: with diets to 'make her better'. But in the real world, however thin Juliet was it didn't seem to make life any easier. Bingeing and being sick became her expression of not coping, a way of escaping from tough everyday realities.

'I don't understand how she could do this,' her mother complained. 'She never lacked my time, attention or affection as a child, nor the material things her friends had.'

Although Juliet loved her mother deeply, her worst binges always came after a trip home or a visit from her mother. The hardest change of all for her to make was to loosen the suffocating strings of love that tied her to her childhood. Yet as she matured and learned to become a complete person in her own right she was able to put her eating problems behind her.

Even in these more enlightened days, far too many girls are still brought up under the general assumption that they should not put themselves forward, that a woman's place is second place. Older women in particular grew up to expressions like 'Nice girls don't . . .' and 'People won't like you if . . .' Boys also encounter influences in their lives that cause them to lack self-confidence, perhaps being goaded at school with 'Boys must grow up to be the bread-winners' or 'Boys don't cry.'

MOTHERHOOD

If a girl grows up to be a mother herself she can find the other side of the fence just as difficult. Years spent alone at home with young children can turn out to be far more demanding than a woman expects when she is excited about starting a family. Sleepless nights, noisy demands for attention, isolation and a lack of money and privacy all add up to a lot of stress.

Although young children need a lot of their mother's time and attention it need not become a 24-hour-a-day, seven-day-a-week job. In fact the mother and child relationship is likely to be a lot happier if the mother is able to take some time off for physical and emotional refreshment. Don't feel guilty about sending your toddler to a nursery or childminder. He is likely to benefit from having his horizons broadened and will be extra pleased to see you when you return. There are also very competent people well able to mind your baby in a crèche for an hour while you take part in an exercise class. Exchanging babysitting favours with a friend can benefit you both.

When the children are older it becomes even more important that they learn see their mother as a person in her own right and are taught to respect her right to a life of her own alongside her important role as their mother. Children who learn this kind of respect for their parents are more likely to treat other people they meet in life with respect and consideration. If they have got used to thinking of their mother as a doormat – because that is the image she projects – they are being set up for unsatisfactory relationships in later years.

Bridget lived in the country and so she found herself spending a large part of each day chauffeuring her three children around. She became very resentful of never having any time to herself. When she moved to live in town and the children could walk to school or catch a bus to wherever they wanted to go she was amazed at the difference it made to her life. With this stressful load lifted from her she found she liked her children a lot more and family life became more of a pleasure and less of a chore.

Jennifer wanted to move house to be nearer to her children's schools and her workplace. She couldn't move, however, because mortgages were high and no one was buying property. She let her home instead, renting a place nearer where she wanted to live. She was much happier and so were her children.

The years fly quickly and one day the children are grown up and leaving home. A mother who has devoted herself totally to their wants and needs, neglecting herself, can suddenly find her life empty and meaningless. It's a wise woman who retains her own identity rather than just thinking of herself as someone's mum.

DIFFICULT PARTNERSHIPS

A partner of someone whose life is dominated by food may not know what is wrong, only that his loved one suffers mysterious mood swings. He may know that an eating problem exists and that he cannot expect rational behaviour or common sense when his partner is in the grip of an urge to binge, but may have no idea how to help.

Lack of patience, non-acceptance or withdrawal of love may make the situation worse, driving the compulsive eater deeper within herself and further into the tangled web of her relationship with food and eating.

If a partner genuinely wants to help but at the same time supports the eating habit – perhaps by buying special binge food – he may be doing more harm than good, even with the best of motives. However, in many cases a partner has a vested emotional interest in keeping his wife, girlfriend or daughter shackled to her food obsession. He wants to keep her dependent on him, which keeps them both entrenched in the security of their negative lifestyle. They become mutually dependent.

Carla had been a compulsive eater for years, until she reached a point when she decided she was going to make changes. With the support of an eating plan and regular counselling she gradually began to get to grips with the things that were causing her to binge. She found a well-balanced diet made a tremendous difference to her sense of well-being after nearly 20 years of dieting and bingeing. Over a period of several months she lost weight, began to look younger and healthier and started taking an interest in the outside world.

All was going really well. Carla was enrolled at college to update her rusty secretarial skills and was beginning to make friends and go out in the evenings. Then everything began to go wrong.

Carla's husband Ron was happy for her to try and get her eating under control. Fed up with years of moodiness and food obsessions from Carla he agreed it was a good idea for her to try and stop her bingeing habits. He thought that if it worked (and he didn't really believe it would anyway) he would end up with the same old Carla but someone a bit easier to live with. It never occurred to him that truly getting her eating under control would in fact change his wife almost beyond recognition. When he began to see a whole new personality emerging he started to panic.

It made him anxious to look at his formerly drab wife and see someone with an attractive smile and a lively sparkle in her eyes. He began to feel very insecure when Carla, who had always been around the house cooking, eating or watching television, started going out in the evenings and spending time chatting on the phone. The happier and more outgoing she became, the more his *own* insecurities deepened and the more depressed he got.

They started to argue. He criticized and belittled everything she did and was constantly in a black mood. Finally he telephoned her counsellor in a furious temper, blaming her for the changes in his wife. 'She doesn't need me any longer. What am I supposed to do?' he raged.

Their relationship had reached a crossroads. They had to settle their differences, go their separate ways, or sink back into their old familiar rut. Carla chose the difficult route of making a new life for herself on her own. She struggled for three tough years, facing up to the many challenges of surviving alone and not falling back into the binge trap. She met Maurice, who had never known the 'old' Carla. They married and lived a much better and more fulfilling life than Carla and Ron had ever known.

Ron, on the other hand, refused to make any personal changes. In time he married a woman who suffered from many of the problems Carla had once had. He recreated for himself the safe, familiar world he craved in spite of the fact that it brought him little happiness.

Ron needed a wife with an eating problem to make him feel needed. That was his security. This kind of relationship makes it impossible for one partner to overcome a problem and still keep the old-style partnership intact. Both partners have problems with self-respect: each must tackle his or her individual difficulties before they can build a new type of relationship.

There are two distinct types of people who become drawn into mutually dependent relationships. On the one hand are those who feel they have no real identity of their own and need a stronger person to live their lives through. These are the ones who stay in difficult or abusive relationships because they have no concept of surviving alone.

On the other hand there are the caretakers, those who need someone weaker than themselves to look after to give them a valid role in life. They may devote themselves totally to an elderly relative, alcoholic partner or their children, never looking for anything beyond this.

Both types lack any sense of their own self-worth. Nearly always, this can be traced back to their childhood. Children of dysfunctional families – where one or both parents have had problems with alcohol, drugs or eating – invariably slip into similar roles when they become adults. Without realizing what is happening they seek out a partner who supports this role – and the pattern is continued.

Cynthia played out this scenario with her daughter. Herself the child of an alcoholic she became bulimic and, following the break-up of her marriage, centred her whole life around looking after her daughter Beth. As Beth grew from teenager to young adult the roles became reversed: Beth was the one who needed to care for her mother to give her life some meaning while Cynthia existed only as a part of Beth's life.

Cynthia began attending group sessions to come to terms with her bulimia and learned about what is sometimes called 'co-dependency'. Both mother and daughter then joined a programme to tackle the difficulties in their relationship. In this way, in time, they were able to loosen the suffocating bonds between them and each developed a full life and personality of her own.

People like Cynthia find it very hard to relate to others: either they are anti-social and hide away from the world or they are too social, becoming involved with the wrong people, talking too much, saying inappropriate things or acting in a grandiose way to try to cover their perceived inadequacies. Both types find it difficult to make true friends. They are difficult to get close to and end up lonely and isolated.

PATTERNS OF ADDICTION

The association between dysfunctional families and addiction is common. The idea grew out of the realization that the partners of alcoholics often need as much help as the alcoholics themselves. The partners of those addicted to alcohol, drugs or food may themselves be 'addicted' to the negative life they exist in; the two are bound together in perpetuating a mutually destructive relationship.

In this way it is easy to see how the wife of an alcoholic may turn to compulsive eating as a way of coping with her life. His drinking excuses her bingeing, and eventually her bingeing becomes another excuse for his drinking.

When coming to terms with an eating problem many people are surprised to discover how much dependency in relationships influences their lives. Their programme for getting back in control of their eating often has to include coming to terms with negative relationships. Where a damaging relationship - with a partner, child, parent or friend - is used as an excuse for bingeing and at the same time seems the reason for bingeing, it has to be tackled before eating can really be brought under control.

AVOIDING RELATIONSHIPS

Eating can be a way of avoiding relationships if there is some deep-seated reason for keeping the world away. A woman who is afraid of a particular man or of men in general may become totally taken up with her food compulsion so there is no room for boyfriends or marriage. Have you ever thought any of the following?:

1. I am too fat to attract a man.
2. I will meet the right man when I am at my ideal weight.
3. I can't handle my eating so I could not handle a relationship.
4. I can't get close to anyone in case they find out about my bingeing.
5. I am not ready to make a commitment to anyone.

If any of these statements seems to fit, you could be using your eating compulsion to avoid relationships. It is common for women to tell themselves the 'right' man will come along when they have got over their eating problems, or when they reach their ideal weight, at the same time continually bingeing so that they ensure that day never arrives.

Size and weight have nothing at all to do with meeting an ideal partner, unless you choose to make it an obstacle. Lots of overweight people are happily married with lots of friends, as are lots of slim people - weight is just a convenient cover-up for deeper difficulties.

While some compulsive eaters have no relationships because there is no room in their lives for anything but their food obsession, others have many relationships, sometimes to the extent of promiscuity, but nothing that ever advances beyond the physical and the temporary. These are the women who are unable to commit even a corner of themselves to another person. As soon as there is any sign of an emotional attachment they withdraw.

UNHAPPY RELATIONSHIPS

Staying put in a relationship that isn't working often seems easier than facing the traumas of breaking up and being on your own again. Too many people stay with the wrong person because they believe they cannot survive on their own. Invariably this is not true. A partner who only adds to your feelings of low self-esteem is holding you back, acting as a dead weight. You are most likely to find life a lot easier when you have only yourself to look after, but you won't discover the truth of this until you take the plunge. If you are wondering whether your current relationship is worth sticking with, try answering the questionnaire below.

Table 21 IS THERE A FUTURE IN MY RELATIONSHIP?

	No/ Never	Rarely	Often	Yes/ Always
1. Do I enjoy being with my partner?	☐	☐	☐	☐
2. Am I afraid to communicate my feelings when we are together?	☐	☐	☐	☐
3. Do I feel uncomfortable when my partner is present?	☐	☐	☐	☐
4. Am I staying in this relationship because I am afraid of being alone?	☐	☐	☐	☐
5. Am I deciding not to quit the relationship just to protect my partner from pain?	☐	☐	☐	☐
6. Would I leave this relationship if I wasn't afraid of what others would think?	☐	☐	☐	☐
7. Will my family be upset if I finish this relationship?	☐	☐	☐	☐
8. Will my partner's family be upset if I finish this relationship?	☐	☐	☐	☐
9. Are my strong views about relationships and marriage affecting my decision to quit or stay?	☐	☐	☐	☐
10. Do I believe 'marriage is forever'?	☐	☐	☐	☐
11. Do I believe my relationship might work if we went for counselling — but my partner won't come with me?	☐	☐	☐	☐

	No/ Never	Rarely	Often	Yes/ Always
12. Am I happier when I am without my partner?	☐	☐	☐	☐
13. Is my partner expecting too much from me?	☐	☐	☐	☐
14. Is there little chance that things can change for the better?	☐	☐	☐	☐
15. Will either my physical or mental health be hurt if I stay?	☐	☐	☐	☐

Calculate your score as follows:
No/Never = 0, Rarely = 1, Often = 2, Yes/Always = 3.

SCORING

Less than 5. You know what you want and need out of a relationship and you seem to be achieving it.

6–25. Don't believe that this relationship is the only way for you to live. You may be surprised at how better the world is on the outside, but alternatively you may find you can improve the relationship you are in by becoming more self-confident and assertive about your wants and needs.

Over 26. Should you really be in this relationship? You could be staying in it for the wrong reasons, probably to protect yourself or others from what you believe to be pain. By doing so you may well cause even greater pain either soon or in the future. If you really see no hope for the future why are you hanging on?

If you answered Yes to question 15 you should certainly take immediate action to remove yourself from this potentially dangerous environment. Even if you believe you can work out a good future for the both of you within the relationship, you need to give yourself space and time to think. Remove yourself temporarily.

Having considered whether or not you should be in your current relationship, the next stage is to determine how satisfactory that relationship is. Try the questionnaire which follows.

Table 22 HOW SATISFACTORY IS MY RELATIONSHIP?

	Yes	No
1. Are you putting more into the relationship than you are getting out of it?	☐	☐

                                                                    Yes   No

2. Do you usually feel at ease when you are with your
   partner?   ☐   ☐

3. Do you feel that your partner enjoys being around you?   ☐   ☐

4. Does your partner openly express appreciation of the
   things you do for him/her?   Often/Sometimes/Never

5. Does your partner criticize you in front of others?
                                                 Often/Sometimes/Never

6. Do you feel your partner emphasizes your mistakes and
   ignores your achievements?   ☐   ☐

7. Does your partner often refuse to speak to you?   ☐   ☐

8. Does your partner often lose his/her temper with you?   ☐   ☐

9. Is your partner supportive most of the time?   ☐   ☐

10. Do you often do things together that you both enjoy?   ☐   ☐

11. Is your sex life mutually satisfying?   ☐   ☐

SCORING

1. Yes = 4; No = 0.

2. Yes = 0; No = 4.

3. Yes = 0; No = 4.

4. Often = 0; Sometimes = 2; Never = 4.

5. Often = 4; Sometimes = 2; Never = 0.

6. Yes = 4; No = 0.

7. Yes = 4; No = 0.

8. Yes = 4; No = 0.

9. Yes = 0; No = 4.

10. Yes = 0; No = 4.

11. Yes = 0; No = 4.

Less than 10. You have an excellent relationship, make sure you both
work at keeping it so good.

11-20. Your relationship has a lot of good points and although
there are a few things you could work on, generally
things look promising.

Over 21. There is a lot about your relationship that is not
satisfactory. You need to think carefully about why you
are staying in this relationship; perhaps you should even
be rethinking whether you should remain in the
relationship or not.

WHEN TO QUIT

With every difficult relationship there comes a point when you have to decide whether there is anything left to salvage or whether the time has come for you to go your separate ways. This need not mean a lot of pain for all involved, although sadly it often does.

Parents have to accept that their children grow up and move away into their own lives, although even then it is still quite possible for a close, loving relationship to flourish. When a couple grows apart it can be more difficult to remain on good terms, although it is usually worth the effort, especially if children are involved.

To carry on being friends with someone you once had a close involvement with can take a lot of self-assertiveness. You have to believe truly that you have the right to a life of your own. You must work through any feelings of guilt and anger you might have. This will be very difficult if you are bingeing and/or hiding your emotions in a food obsession. Overcoming your eating problems and sorting out current and outworn relationships in your life are closely related and need to be worked out together. One cannot be tackled effectively if the other is ignored.

16 Choosing to Change

The decisions you made in the past may have been coloured by the people and circumstances around you at the time, but whenever there was a choice to be made you were the one who made it. All the time you go on blaming others for the things you don't like about your life you are making another choice ~ choosing not to take responsibility for yourself.

Give up blaming your mother because you were a tubby child. Yes, your mother may have offered you more food than you needed and allowed you to develop your natural love of sweet things, but now you are an adult you can choose what you do and do not eat.

Give up blaming your boss because your job is boring and you hate the idea of turning up at the office each day. You chose to take that job in the first place. You are free to hand in your notice tomorrow if you choose to accept the consequences of being unemployed or looking for another job.

Give up blaming your partner because he contributes so little to your relationship that you are miserable and binge. You chose to be in the relationship and you chose your attitude towards him and towards the lifestyle you both lead. If it has not worked out exactly as you wanted make changes to create something different in the future. At the moment it is you who is choosing not to change and to stay miserable.

- You are choosing not to get help with your depression.
- You are choosing to live under too much stress.
- You are choosing not to face up to being afraid of change.
- You are choosing to allow yourself to feel guilty.
- You are choosing not to get help with your drinking.
- You are choosing not to get help with your eating problem.

Your life is a tiny island in a large world. Why make that island a hostile place when it could be cosy and friendly?

While tackling the physical side of the problem there is plenty you can be doing at the same time to clear out the debris of negative thoughts and habits that have built up during your time as a compulsive eater.

BOREDOM

The more energy and effort you put into something, the more you get out of it. If all your reserves have been poured into dealing with your eating disorder, no wonder you have had nothing left to give to more positive interests.

With the freedom from food and weight obsession, the Eating Plan will give you an extra pool of energy to invest in new interests or in pepping up the flagging ones you already have.

TELEVISION

Try turning off the television. Television is a very potent force in our lives. Like anything that exerts an influence it picks its most willing victims from among those who lack the ability to make the best of their lives and those with problems they are unable to face. Television is the ultimate alternative to real life. Just sit there and soak up the easy option that fills all emotional gaps and blanks out uncomfortable realities.

Television wields its influence in two ways. First, the habit of sitting in front of the set becomes a way of life that is less than satisfying. Second, the images that are projected through programmes, and in particular through advertising, greatly influence our thought patterns and living habits.

Perhaps you do not really appreciate just how much television you watch. It is easy to convince yourself you are just going to watch one favourite programme and then to end up sitting in front of the set for three or four hours. Try working on the questions which follow to see just how much of a telly addict you have become.

Table 23 ARE YOU A TELLY ADDICT?

	Yesterday	Last Week
1. How many hours of television did you watch?	☐	☐
2. For how many hours did you have the television on without watching it or while doing something else?	☐	☐
3. How many programmes did you watch because you really wanted to see them?	☐	☐
4. How many programmes did you begin watching and become deeply engrossed in?	☐	☐
5. How many programmes did you begin watching and lose interest in but still did not turn off?	☐	☐
6. How many programmes were so engrossing you did not think about food?	☐	☐
7. How much time did you spend watching television because you had nothing else to do?	☐	☐
8. How much time did you spend watching television to escape doing something else?	☐	☐
9. How many times did you put off doing something or going somewhere because you wanted to watch television?	☐	☐
10. How many times did you watch television because you felt too tired to do anything else?	☐	☐
11. How many times did you envy a character on television or think someone you saw on television had a better life than you?	☐	☐
12. How often did television influence your choice of food?	☐	☐
13. How often did you eat in front of the television?	☐	☐
14. How often did you binge in front of the television?	☐	☐
	Total =	Total =

Television is a habit and so is compulsive eating – in fact the two often go together. The answers you gave for the last three questions in Table 23 could show how closely eating and television are linked in your life. Eating while watching television means that what goes in through your mouth tends to take second place to what is going in through your eyes and ears. This is a particular danger for those who live alone or spend too much time alone with the television. It is too easy to get into the habit of putting food in your mouth without really being aware of how much you are eating. If eating and bingeing often occur when the television is on, simply switching the set off is not going to cure your compulsive eating – but it could well be a major step towards making some very necessary changes.

What would you do if you were not watching television?

Perhaps you would talk more to those you live with; lack of communication is a common element in the breakdown of relationships. How often does your family sit round and have a good chat or discuss important issues? How often do your children sit round the table for a family meal and appreciate the food you have prepared for them? When did you and your partner last talk properly to each other about how you are feeling and about your relationship? All the time the television is on, communication is stifled.

The television habit can completely ruin your social life and eventually isolate you from society. How often have you put off going to visit friends because it would mean missing a good film? Or decided against joining an evening class because it was held on the same night as your favourite programme?

There have been plenty of suggestions made in this book for alternative things to do to help break the bingeing habit. A lot of people will have said they have not got time to join a class, go to a workshop, make new social contacts or take up a hobby – but they seem to have plenty of time for watching television. Television watching is easy, it takes absolutely no effort to switch on the set and sit in front of it, endless 'entertainment' on tap. An hour of aerobics, two hours of pottery, a weekend of self-assertiveness takes a lot more effort – but these things are far more rewarding and are the keys to a new, more satisfying life. When you are eating a balanced, nourishing diet you will find you have the energy to do these things and more.

Could you live without your television set? Probably the thought secretly horrifies you, because a house without a television set would be quiet enough to bring you face-to-face with emotions, relationships and problems that are being drowned out at the moment. Try turning the television off and see what happens. How do you feel? What response do you get from the rest of the household? Can you cope with the full force of their attention, which has been directed elsewhere for so long? Or if you live alone, can you stand the silence?

Sometimes it is not really your problem. Perhaps your partner wants to watch television and likes to have you in the room. The answer could be to use a pair of headphones so you can listen to music, or to develop an interesting hobby to pursue while the television is on. Or perhaps you could negotiate a compromise of times when you watch together and times when you have the freedom to do as you please.

RISK FACTORS

Turning off the television can be a real act of bravery and defiance. You are taking the risk of having to face up to yourself and being fully aware of how you are spending your time.

As mentioned earlier, these sort of risks are all around you when you decide to make important changes to improve your life. Opening the doors is a big risk. You really don't know what you might find on the other side. But only by taking that risk will you find out.

- Accepting a challenge is taking a risk.
- Accepting the need for change is taking a risk.
- Accepting things could be better is taking a risk.
- Accepting you can handle whatever comes next is taking a risk.
- Making a positive move is taking a risk.
- Improving your self-esteem is taking a risk.
- By taking a risk you earn the respect of others.

FEAR OF FAILURE

Fear of failure leads to a fear of attempting anything that seems to hold the slightest risk. Life becomes more and more limited as it is restricted to activities and surroundings that are familiar. Low self-esteem, which as has been said again and again is at the root of many compulsive eating problems, feeds this fear of failure so that thoughts of food and weight become the only familiar ground and everything else becomes a threatening challenge.

The student who is afraid of failing her exams ... binges

The woman who feels unattractive and fears to go out or enter relationships in case they don't work ... binges

The man who avoids seeking promotion because he fears he will not get the job ... binges

The woman who fears visiting her parents because she feels a failure in their eyes ... binges.

FEAR OF SUCCESS

Fear of failure, of being held up to public ridicule or merely feeling a failure in your own eyes, is an obvious reason for not attempting something. If you don't try, instead just sitting back and complaining about how tough life is or hiding in a corner and blaming others, then you can *never* succeed.

It is much tougher to be a success. Fear of success can be as great a reason for not trying as fear of failure.

The same man who does not try for promotion in case he fails to get it could equally well not be putting himself forward in case he *does* get it. He may be afraid he would not be able do the job, wouldn't be able to handle the extra pressure or cope with the additional workload. Therefore he finds it easier to stay where he is.

Fear of success is not always obvious. There may well be times when you don't recognize the true nature of the emotion that is holding you back from achieving your ambitions.

Christine is an example of this. She was a very ambitious person and desperately wanted to be a success. She wanted to be a company director, she wanted to live in a six-bedroomed house, she wanted to have a slender figure. In fact she never actually achieved any of these things because she was not prepared to compromise in the way she went about getting them.

She refused to take a minor role in a company because only a directorship had enough status, therefore she was out of work. She refused to buy a one-bedroom flat as a starter home from which she could work her way up the property ladder, because only a large house fitted her ideal, therefore she continued to live at home with her parents.

When it came to her eating habits she set herself a strict macrobiotic diet and refused to compromise by allowing herself a less rigid regime, so her life was an endless see-saw between controlled eating and out of control bingeing which left her disgusted with herself and overweight.

Christine was sabotaging every hope she had of achieving success by setting herself impossibly high standards. At one level she was aware she could never really aspire to such impossible heights. This part of her took some comfort in the fact that she would never be called upon to live the kind of life she felt inadequate to sustain.

If all or any of the following situations tend to drive you to binge, consider some ways in which you might handle them if you were successful at getting over your compulsive eating.

1. You are left alone in the evening. Your husband is working late, the children are in bed, you have had a bad day.

    As a compulsive eater you binge.

    As a successful controlled eater:

    (a) You call up a friend and have a laugh over the telephone.

    (b) You have a luxurious perfumed bath, restyle your hair and give yourself a manicure.

    (c) You sort out your wardrobe and throw out all the baggy, unflattering clothes you used to wear when you did not like yourself.

    (d) You cut out the pattern for a new dress you are making for yourself.

    (e) You write your thoughts down in a journal or do something creative.

2. You have had another argument with your mother. She told you she didn't understand you and that you were impossibly difficult, a total failure, a disappointment to the family.

    As a compulsive eater you binge.

    As a successful controlled eater:

    (a) You telephone or visit a sympathetic friend who always cheers you up.

    (b) You write down all the grievances your mother has against you. When you have finished, re-read the list and mark which of her criticisms you think may be true and which may be due to her own personal limitations.

    (c) You put on some relaxing music, sit comfortably and use

techniques for relaxation and meditation you have learned to calm yourself and regain your positive self-image.

(d) You go out and have a vigorous game of tennis or try to beat your personal best distance for swimming at the local pool.

(e) You calm down, think things through, then either telephone your mother and have a reasonable discussion or write her a letter explaining your side.

3. You are under pressure at work to complete a contract on time and feel obliged to stay late each evening so that by the time you get home you are too exhausted to do anything but flop in a chair.

As a compulsive eater your binge.

As a successful controlled eater:

(a) You stop on the way home to eat a good nourishing meal cooked and served by someone else, or you pick up a well-balanced ready-prepared meal at the supermarket, a salad and some fruit. You tell yourself you have worked hard and deserve to be looked after.

(b) You keep a careful note of all the overtime you do and if your firm does not pay extra, book time off in lieu when the present crisis is over. As an employee you have the right to this. If you are the boss you have the right to allow yourself this.

(c) You work late one day but the next day explain you have an important engagement and must leave on time. You go home without feeling guilty and know things will be fine when you get in the next morning.

(d) You realize that this is not just a one-off emergency, you are going to be under similar pressure all the time. You begin looking around for a better, less pressurized job.

A POSITIVE VIEW

The difference between the bingeing reaction and any of the other reactions is that hiding in a binge is a negative approach to life whereas doing something about a situation is a positive approach.

No matter what your problem is it can be faced by taking a positive approach and refusing to allow yourself to make excuses.

Whenever you catch yourself thinking a negative thought or making a negative statement you have to stop yourself and turn that thought into something positive. It is very difficult at first but in time it does become a habit. For example:

Negative thought: I can't face getting out of bed this morning.

Positive thought: I'm so tired this morning because I stayed up too late last night. I must get up and do something. I'll have an early night tonight.

Negative thought: Nobody likes me.

Positive thought: The woman at work who picked on me today doesn't like me. But I don't like her much, she is just not my type and I think she has a lot of personal problems. What a good thing I have other friends. I think I'll phone someone nice whom I haven't seen for a while.

Negative thought: I'll never stop bingeing.

Positive thought: I missed lunch and my blood sugar levels dropped, so it is not surprising my body was demanding to be fed. This has proved to me beyond all doubt that not eating regularly makes me binge. Now I know this for sure I feel more motivated to feed myself appropriately.

This is how positive thinking works. Now use the same formula to work on your own negative thoughts and statements.

STEP BY STEP

Perhaps you are just being too critical of yourself. Nobody can be perfect all the time, so while always striving for success it is also essential to be able to accept some failure. If you feel all your efforts have failed, review exactly how bad things were before you started and assess how far you have come since then. For this reason it is a good idea to keep some sort of log of your progress. You may like to write a daily diary, being sure to emphasize your positive efforts - perhaps by awarding yourself stars - or you may prefer to draw up a chart on which you can plot your progress in a visual way. Put this chart up somewhere where you can see it every day so it can inspire you to keep going forward.

On Figure 9 plot your progress by moving a pin from left to right. Every time you have a good day you move the pin forward one step towards your goal of success. When you reach day ten you have successfully completed the first stage of your journey and you will be ready to start again at stage two, and so on for as long as you choose your journey to be. The golden rule is that you are never allowed to put the pin back, so when you have a bad day you do not record it as a setback, just as a slight delay on your journey forwards.

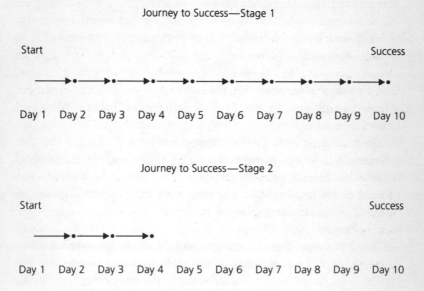

Figure 9 *Journey to Success*

ASSERTIVENESS TRAINING

Assertiveness training courses have helped many, many people develop the confidence to communicate their feelings directly and honestly. They learn to respect their own needs and values and, through this, find they enhance their relationships with others and improve their prospects at work.

Many people confuse the idea of assertiveness with aggressiveness, until they discover that being assertive is very different. Assertiveness is about valuing yourself so you discover the confidence to speak up when a situation demands, not only to ask for what you need but to say no to things you do not need in your life. Assertiveness is not about being angry or confrontational, offensive or negative with yourself or others.

Adult education centres often include assertiveness training courses in their programmes – otherwise look out for courses advertised in your local paper or in health food stores, new age shops and natural health centres. Magazines that deal with personal development subjects are also likely to carry advertisements for such courses, but these may not be held locally.

The following exercise has had a positive effect on me and many of my clients. It is an excellent way of beginning to understand how to regain control of your life:

Find yourself a large, empty jar, the largest one you can find. Then get a large pad of paper. Write each of your hopes, dreams, fears and obstacles on a piece of paper, using a separate sheet for each one. Use different coloured pens for the different feelings/ambitions, if you like. For example, on one page you may write 'anger', on another 'resentment' or 'jealousy', on others stifled feelings such as 'love' or 'laughter'. Or you can set down more specific elements such as 'bingeing', 'going on holiday', 'office promotion', 'anger at parents'.

Fold or scrunch up each sheet and force it into the jar. Think while you are doing this: how does it make you feel? Do you feel a certain amount of control over these emotions as you stuff them one by one into the jar? Once the jar can hold no more, screw on the top (or put in the cork).

The jar represents you – and your life. It is a physical representation of all your pent-up potential and anguish. When you look in the jar it is impossible to tell one sheet from the others, the positive from the negative.

Now think about the stopper on the jar. What does it represent? It is the barrier that is preventing the emotions from getting out and preventing you (as well as anyone else) from getting at them. All the negative emotions are crushing and stifling the positive ones.

You have put the stopper on the jar so that no one can see what is going on. Different people have different stoppers 'plugging up' their lives. Yours is food.

Now you have a choice. You can hide the jar away in a dark corner where no one will find it. It may stay there indefinitely, or it may explode as the contents ferment and bubble away inside. *Or*, you can remove the stopper and face what is inside, removing one piece of paper at a time, gradually. At your own pace, take the risk of finding a negative – or a positive – thought or emotion and dealing with it in an appropriate manner.

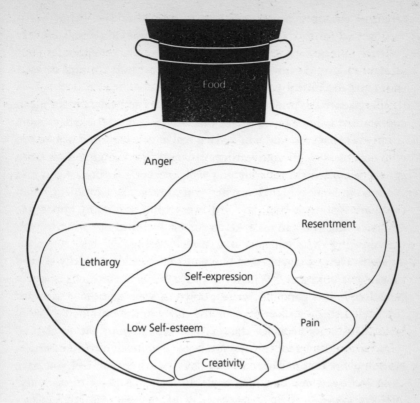

Figure 10

Gradually, as the jar's contents diminish and finally disappear altogether there will be no need to replace the stopper. You will have worked through what was inside. Your need for an eating problem will also have disappeared.

BE PATIENT

Many compulsive eaters are very impatient in their search for a cure to their problems. They want instant success and cannot accept the fact that nobody is going to wave a magic wand and banish their problems overnight. Yet your compulsive eating did not arrive out of the blue one morning. It was a result of years, even a lifetime of wrong eating habits, wrong attitudes and negative thought patterns. Bringing about the fundamental changes in outlook and personality that are the only lasting ways to control compulsive behaviour is a slow and painful business. It is easy to become discouraged. Every setback can be seen as proof of total failure. This exaggerates your fear of failure, destroys your confidence and puts an end to your attempts to control your eating.

It is essential to understand that temporary setbacks do not mean permanent failure. There will be black days. It is on these days more than ever that it is vital you make a real effort. It should not be too difficult to stick to your eating plan and life-changing aims on a good day when things are going well, everyone is nice to you and your confidence is high. It is when you come across a problem, when you are having a bad day and everything seems an impossible struggle that you can really test yourself and find out whether you are meeting the challenges you've set yourself.

Go to the newsagents and buy yourself a packet of sticky-backed silver and gold stars. Whenever you achieve something, however small, or have a good day, write it down in a special book and award yourself a star – a silver star for the day you ate only half a bar of chocolate, a gold star for the day you kept to your eating plan all day, two gold stars for the day you booked yourself into an assertion training workshop. Then on bad days, or when you feel you have lost your way, you can flick back through this book of stars and remind yourself of the huge amount of progress you have in fact made.

If you find yourself giving up as soon as the going gets tough, you have to ask yourself whether you really want to get over your eating problems. Although you may be telling yourself and others that you do want to get your eating under control, deep down are you frightened of changing from the lifestyle you know to something new and possibly very demanding. Be honest with yourself as to whether you are secretly sabotaging yourself.

THE WAY OUT

The Eating Plan is the physical side of getting back in control. Choose to follow the Plan carefully and your body will quickly appreciate the change, giving you more energy, greater stamina, resistance against mood swings and increased confidence as you realize you are losing the urge to binge. The Eating Plan is a very important weapon in your battle to get back in control. You will never truly succeed in overcoming your eating disorder unless you relearn appropriate eating habits. When your body is adequately nourished you will find it much easier to come to terms with all the emotional and life problems that are dragging you down and lowering the quality of your life. You will discover ways to make your life happier and more fulfilling, which will minimize your urge to binge. You will be lifted on an upward spiral that is the complete reverse of the way you were.

The compulsive eater who does not make changes to her life may be afraid of facing a world without her food obsession. What does she put in that void where thoughts of food, eating and weight used to be? This is the view from the inside looking out, but it changes radically once you are on the outside and have expanded your horizons.

Escaping from the isolation of the diet/binge cycle means choosing to walk out. You are not really trapped at all, there are a lot of doors marked *Exit* but you are choosing not to use any of them.

Sounds too easy? It *is* easy. Once you have made the break and are back on the outside again you will wonder why on earth you didn't do it years ago.

Good luck.

5

Extra Help

17 Taking a Maisner Centre Course

Maisner Centre courses can take the form of personal consultation or be carried out by post and telephone, although Paulette does prefer to meet every client at least once if possible. People from all over the world do postal courses; those who live at a distance from the Brighton base of the Maisner Centre have the opportunity to see Maisner counsellors in other parts of Britain.

The first stage of the course is to complete a confidential detailed questionnaire from which each client can be individually assessed. Then the client begins following the Eating Plan detailed in Chapter 5, with its emphasis on small regular meals of good quality food and plenty of protein.

Unlike a typical slimming diet, nobody is expected to stick rigidly to the Plan at first. If you could do that you would not really have an eating problem warranting help. By filling in daily food charts (logging not just what food has been eaten but when, where and why), Paulette and her staff can build up a picture of what is going wrong and from this begin to offer you guidance about how to put things right.

Clients are encouraged to listen regularly to a special cassette recording that covers eating problems on one side and general stress and positive thinking on the other. They are also encouraged to telephone whenever they have a problem they feel they cannot handle and to write in regularly sending their food charts and any other comments they wish to make. This very personal service for a very personal problem has proved successful time and time again.

For further details about the Maisner Centre and other courses that help with eating disorders, send a large s.a.e. to:

PO Box 464
Hove
East Sussex BN3 2BN
Tel. (0273) 729818 or 29334

Recommended Reading

Addicts and Addictions, Dr Vernon Coleman (Corgi, 1987).
The Aerobics Way, Kenneth H. Cooper, M.D., M.P.H. (Transworld, 1978).
The Body Clock Diet, Ronald Gatty, Ph.D. (Simon & Schuster, 1980).
Body, Mind and Sugar, E. M. Abrahamson, M.D. and A. W. Pezet (Holt, Rinehart and Winston, 1960).
Breaking All the Rules, Nancy Roberts (Penguin, 1985).
Jane Brody's Nutrition Book, Jane Brody (W. W. Norton, 1981).
Bulimarexia, Marlene Boskind-White, Ph.D. and William C. White, Jr, Ph.D. (George J. McLeod).
Competing with the Sylph, L. M. Vincent, M.D. (Andrews & McMeel).
The Composition of Foods, A. A. Paul and D. A. T. Southgate (HMSO, 1978).
Coping with Bulimia, Barbara French (Thorsons, 1987).
Depression, Dr Caroline Shreeve (Thorsons, 1984).
The Dieter's Dilemma, William Bennet, M.D. and Joel Gurin (Basic Books).
Dieting Makes You Fat, Geoffrey Cannon and Hetty Einzig (Century, 1983).
Eating is Okay, Henry A. Jordan, M.D., Leonard S. Levitz, Ph.D. and Gordon M. Kimbrell, Ph.D. (Rawson Associates, 1976).
Excuses Won't Cure You, Paulette Maisner with Alison Cridland (Unwin, 1987).
Feasting and Fasting, Paulette Maisner with Jenny Pulling (Fontana, 1985).
Feel the Fear and Do It Anyway, Susan Jeffers (Century, 1987).
Fit or Fat?, Covert Bailey (Pelham, 1980).
The Food Trap, Paulette Maisner with Rosemary Turner (Allen & Unwin, 1985).
Knowing When to Quit: How to Stop Fighting Losing Battles and Get on with Your Life, Jack Barranger (Thorsons, 1991).

Let's Eat Right to Keep Fit, Adelle Davis (Unwin, 1984).

Life is an Elevator, Paulette Maisner with Rosemary Turner (Lennard, 1989).

Low Blood Sugar, Martin Budd (Thorsons, 1981).

Making the Most of Yourself, Gill Cox and Sheila Dainow (Sheldon, 1985).

Men Who Hate Women and the Women Who Love Them, Dr Susan Forward (Bantam, 1986).

Not All in the Mind, Dr Richard Mackarness (Pan, 1982).

Once a Month, Katharina Dalton (Fontana, 1978).

The Premenstrual Syndrome, Dr Caroline Shreeve (Thorsons, 1992).

Release from Nervous Tension, D. H. Fink (Unwin, 1984).

Sugar Blues, William Dufty (Abacus, 1980).

The Superwoman Trap and How to Escape It, Cathy Douglas (Futura, 1984).

Taking the Rough with the Smooth, Dr Andrew Stanway (Pan, 1981).

Treat Obesity Seriously, J. S. Garrow (Churchill Livingstone).

Why Do I Think I Am Nothing without a Man?, Penelope Russianoff, Ph.D. (Bantam, 1983).

A Woman in Your Own Right, Anne Dickson (Quartet, 1982).

A number of these books are available from the Maisner Centre bookshop. For a complete list please send a stamped addressed envelope to:

PO Box 464
Hove
East Sussex BN3 2BN

Appendix

Food Tables

Table 24 CALORIE AND PROTEIN CONTENT OF CERTAIN FOODS

	Kcals per 100 g/3.5 oz	Protein per 100 g/3.5 oz
MEAT		
Bacon		
gammon rashers, lean, grilled	172	31.4
middle rashers, lean and fat, grilled	416	24.1
Beef		
mince, stewed	229	23.1
stewing steak, stewed, lean and fat	223	30.9
topside roast, lean and fat	214	26.6
Chicken		
boiled, meat only	183	29.2
leg, quarter (weighed with bone)	92	15.4
roast, meat only	148	24.8
(Turkey has slightly less calories and amount of protein)		
Lamb		
breast, roast, lean only	252	25.6
chops, lean and fat, grilled	355	23.5
leg, roast, lean and fat	266	26.1
shoulder, roast, lean and fat	316	19.9
Offal		
kidney, lamb, raw weight	90	16.5
liver, lamb, raw weight	179	20.1
ox tail, stewed	243	30.5
Pork		
chops, grilled, lean and fat	332	28.5
leg, roast, lean only	185	30.7

	Kcals per 100 g/3.5 oz	Protein per 100 g/3.5 oz
FISH		
Cod		
grilled	95	20.8
poached	94	20.9
Haddock		
smoked, steamed	101	23.3
steamed	98	22.8
Herring		
grilled	199	20.4
Sardines		
in oil	289	22.8
Shellfish		
crab, boiled	127	20.1
mussels, boiled	87	17.2
prawns, boiled	107	22.6
Trout		
brown, steamed	135	23.5
Tuna		
in oil	289	22.8

NON-ANIMAL PROTEIN FOODS

bologna*	167	20.0
dinner balls*	225	14.0
liquid soya milk*	51	3.6
nut brawn*	212	8.3
quorn	85	12.3
sausalatas*	137	11.0
soya bean pâté*	132	10.8
soya flour, full-fat	447	36.8
soya flour, low-fat	352	45.3
tofu burgers (Cauldron Foods brand)	187	12.9
TVP: beef flavour*	250	51.5
chicken flavour*	227	46.0
sweet & sour flavour*	250	51.5

* manufactured by Granose Foods Ltd

	Kcals per 100 g/3.5 oz	Protein per 100 g/3.5 oz
DAIRY PRODUCTS		
Butter		
salted	740	0.4
Cheese		
Camembert	300	22.8
Cheddar	406	26.0
Cottage cheese	96	13.6
Edam	304	24.4
Cream		
double	447	1.5
single	212	2.4
whipping	332	1.9
Eggs		
whole, raw	147	12.3
Milk		
fresh, skimmed	33	3.4
fresh, whole	65	3.3
Yogurt		
natural, low-fat	52	5.0
CEREALS		
Bread		
brown	223	8.9
wholemeal	216	8.8
Breakfast Cereal		
porridge, cooked	44	1.4
shredded wheat	324	10.6
wheat bran	206	14.1
VEGETABLES		
butter beans, boiled	95	7.1
green mung beans, raw	231	22.0
haricot beans, boiled	93	6.6
lentils, split, boiled	99	7.5
peas, dried, raw	286	1.6
peas, fresh, boiled	52	5.0
potatoes, old, baked	85	2.1

	Kcals per 100 g/3.5 oz	Protein per 100 g/3.5 oz
potatoes, old, boiled	80	1.4
red kidney beans, boiled	87	22.1
sweetcorn, boiled	123	4.1

FRUITS

avocado pears	223	4.2

NUTS

almonds	565	16.9
brazils	619	12.0
chestnuts	170	2.0
hazelnuts	380	7.6
peanuts	570	24.3
peanut butter	623	22.6
walnuts	525	10.6

Taken from McCance & Widdowson, *The Composition of Foods* (HMSO).

Table 25 HIDDEN SUGARS

	Percentage per 100g
parsnips, raw	8.8
sweetcorn, canned kernels	8.9
apples, eating	9.1
figs, green, raw	9.5
damsons, raw	9.6
plums, dessert, raw	9.6
beetroot, boiled	9.9
onions, fried	10.1
chicken noodle soup, dried	10.2
Coca-Cola	10.5
pears, eating	10.6
pineapple, fresh	11.6
cherries, eating, raw	11.9
nectarines, raw	12.4
currant bread	13.0
soya flour, low-fat	13.4
Kellogg's *All Bran*	15.4
grapes, black, raw	15.5
Bemax	16.0
lychees, raw	16.0
grapes, white, raw	16.1

	Percentage per 100g
bananas, raw	16.2
malt bread	18.6
dairy ice cream	22.6
tomato ketchup	22.9
brown sauce, bottled	23.1
lime juice cordial, undiluted	24.8
fruit salad, canned	25.0
muesli	26.2
orange drink, undiluted	28.5
mince pie	30.0
fruit pie, pastry top and bottom	30.9
cherry brandy	32.6
madeira cake	36.5
prunes, dried, raw	40.3
apricots, dried, raw	43.4
rich fruit cake	46.7
sponge cake, jam-filled	47.7
Horlicks malted milk	49.4
chutney, apple	50.1
figs, green, dried	52.9
peaches, dried, raw	53.0
coffee and chicory essence	53.8
fancy iced cakes	54.0
rich iced fruit cake	54.2
chocolate milk	56.5
Ribena, undiluted	60.9
rosehip syrup, undiluted	61.8
jelly, packet of cubes	62.5
currants, dried	63.1
dates, dried	63.9
raisins, dried	64.4
sultanas, dried	64.7
liquorice allsorts	67.2
jam, fruit with edible seeds	69.0
Ovaltine	73.0
boiled sweets	86.9
meringues	95.6
peppermints	102.2

Taken from McCance & Widdowson, *The Composition of Foods* (HMSO).

Table 26 FOODS RICH IN VITAMINS AND MINERALS

VITAMIN A

butter
cheese
coloured fruits and vegetables
cream

egg yolk
fish liver oil
liver

VITAMIN B COMPLEX

cereals
wheatgerm

whole-grain breads
yeast

RIBOFLAVIN (VITAMIN B$_2$)

cheese
eggs
liver

meat
milk

NIACIN (VITAMIN B$_3$)

legumes

whole-grain cereals

PYRIDOXINE (VITAMIN B$_6$)

blackstrap molasses
bran

liver
vegetables

VITAMIN C

grapefruit juice
orange juice
raw vegetables and fruits

salads
tomato juice

VITAMIN D

fish liver oil
herrings
mackerel

pilchards
sardines
tuna

VITAMIN E

green, leafy vegetables
vegetable oil

wheatgerm

CALCIUM

cheese
green, leafy vegetables
milk

nuts
soya beans
sunflower seeds

CHLORINE

kelp
Olives

table salt

CHROMIUM

Brewer's yeast
chicken
corn oil

meat
shellfish

COPPER

cocoa
egg yolk

liver
nuts

IODINE

kelp
onions

seafood

IRON

cocoa
egg yolk
green vegetables

red meats
wheatgerm
whole-grain cereals

MAGNESIUM

apples
dark green vegetables
figs
grapefruit

lemons
nuts
seeds
yellow corn

MANGANESE

beets
egg yolk
green, leafy vegetables

nuts
peas
whole-grain cereals

PHOSPHORUS

cheese
eggs
fish
meat

milk
nuts
seeds
whole-wheat cereals

POTASSIUM

bananas
citrus fruits
green, leafy vegetables
mint leaves

potatoes
sunflower seeds
watercress

ZINC

Brewer's yeast
eggs
ground mustard
lamb chops
non-fat dried milk

pork loin
pumpkin seeds
round steak
wheatgerm

Adapted from information in Adelle Davis, *Let's Stay Healthy* (Unwin Paperbacks) and Earl Mindell, *The Vitamin Bible* (Arlington Books).

Table 27 HIDDEN FATS

	Percentage per 100g
oil	99.9
butter	82.0
mayonnaise	78.9
peanut butter (smooth)	53.7
walnuts	51.5
peanuts	49.0
cream cheese	47.4
low-fat spread	40.7
sausage roll (with flaky pastry)	36.2
crisps	35.9
bacon, back rashers, grilled	33.8

	Percentage per 100g
Cheddar-type cheese	33.5
onions, fried	33.3
milk chocolate	30.3
sardines, canned in oil	28.3
chocolate-covered biscuits	27.6
salad cream	27.4
pork pie, individual	27.0
pork sausages, grilled	24.6
mushrooms, whole, fried	22.3
avocado pear	22.2
single cream	21.2
steak and kidney pie, individual	21.2
scampi, fried	17.6
beefburgers, fried	17.3
lamb, roast, lean only	16.6
cream crackers	16.3
fruit pie, pastry top and bottom	15.5
lamb chop, grilled, lean only	12.3
pork chop, loin, grilled, lean only	12.3
corned beef	12.1
kipper, baked	11.4
egg, whole, raw	10.9
currant bun	7.6
leg of pork, roast, lean only	6.9
dairy ice cream	6.6
rump steak, grilled, lean only	6.0
roast chicken, meat only	5.4
potatoes, roast	4.8
cottage cheese	4.0
milk, whole	3.8

Taken from McCance & Widdowson, The Composition of Foods (HMSO).

Table 28 HIGH-FIBRE FOODS

	Grammes of Fibre per 100g
wheatbran	44.0
Kellogg's *All Bran**	26.7
haricot beans, raw	25.4
apricots, dried, raw*	24.0
butter beans, raw	21.6
figs, dried, raw*	18.5
instant potatoes, powder	16.5
soya flour, low-fat	14.3
coconut, fresh, kernel only	13.6

	Grammes of Fibre per 100g
shredded wheat	12.3
frozen peas, boiled	12.0
lentils, raw	11.7
Ryvita rye crispbread	11.7

*These foods also have a high sugar content.

Table 29 CONVERSION TABLE: STONES ⮞ KILOS ⮞ POUNDS

A stone equals fourteen avoirdupois pounds, 2.2 pounds is a kilo. In this table kilos have been rounded up to the nearest whole number.

Stones	Kilos	Pounds
6.5	41	91
7.0	45	98
7.5	48	105
8.0	51	112
8.5	54	119
9.0	57	126
9.5	60	133
10.0	64	140
10.5	67	147
11.0	70	154
11.5	73	161
12.0	76	168
12.5	80	175
13.0	83	182
13.5	86	189
14.0	89	196
14.5	92	203
15.0	96	210
15.5	99	217
16.0	102	224
16.5	105	231
17.0	108	238
17.5	111	245
18.0	115	252

Index